A Planet Called Earth

A Planet Called Earth

GEORGE GAMOW

PROFESSOR OF PHYSICS,
UNIVERSITY OF COLORADO

NEW YORK: THE VIKING PRESS

TO

PROFESSOR ARTHUR HOLMES

PREFACE

Twenty-two years ago I wrote a book entitled *Biography of the Earth*, which summarized astronomical, geological, and biological information concerning our globe. Since that time this book has gone through many printings, and has appeared in a pocket edition as well as in a special edition for the Armed Forces fighting on the European and Asian fronts. It has also been translated into a dozen foreign languages.

In 1959 The Viking Press asked me to revise the book for a new printing. But the revision had to be done under very restricting conditions dictated by production costs. I did my best, but it is impossible to rejuvenate a fading beauty by just a few smears of lipstick and pats of the powder puff. Thus, when the "revised" edition appeared it drew sharp criticism from many reviewers, in particular a noted geologist, Arthur Holmes, who in his review in *Nature* called the book "A Farrago of Earth History." And I must admit that in many respects this criticism was justified.

Thus the only solution for me was to sit down and do it the

hard way, rewriting the book completely under a new title and retaining only the parts of the old text pertaining to facts and theories which have not changed since the original writing. And I take pleasure in dedicating this volume to Professor Holmes, with whom I had a friendly correspondence following the appearance of his review.

G. GAMOW

CONTENTS

ILLUSTRATIONS

Illustrations

A Planet Called Earth

O sweet spontaneous
earth how often have
the
doting

     fingers of
prurient philosophers pinched
and
poked

thee
, has the naughty thumb
of science prodded
thy
     beauty   . how
often have religions taken
thee upon their scraggy knees
squeezing and

buffeting thee that thou mightest conceive
gods
     (but
true

to the incomparable
couch of death thy
rhythmic
lover

     thou answerest

them only with

       spring)

          — e. e. cummings

The Earth Is Born

OLD LEGENDS

FROM THE DAWN of prehistory men have tried to understand the world they live in, and various stories of the creation of the world have inevitably been connected with contemporary religious beliefs.

According to the Assyro-Babylonian version, this is what happened: Marduk, who was the son of the fresh-water god Ea, had a big battle with the female dragon Tiamat, representing chaos. Marduk defeated Tiamat's husband, Kingu, and eleven monsters under his command; then he fought and killed Tiamat herself. He cut the body of Tiamat into two halves, using one half to make the firmament, and another to make the Earth. Then Marduk attached the bodies of Kingu and the eleven monsters to the firmament along a broad circular belt, thus forming the signs of the Zodiac, and made the Moon and the planets move along that belt. In the meantime Marduk's father, Ea, used the blood drained from the body of the slain Kingu for making a man to live in the newly created world.

According to the Egyptian story, creation began with the sun god Amon-Ra, who was born of the lotus flower growing on the surface of the primordial ocean. Amon-Ra had three children: a girl named Nut, and two boys called Shu and Keb. It seems that Shu once found his brother and sister tangled in chaos, and in order to straighten things out, lifted the body of Nut high up, leaving Keb stretched below. Thus Nut became the sky, Keb the Earth, and Shu the air which separates them.

The version of creation given in Indian Vedas is less descriptive and more abstract. It starts with the statement that in the beginning there was neither being nor non-being, neither air nor sky, neither death nor immortality, neither night nor day. There was nothing else save the One which breathed, breathless, of its own power. Then through the power of austerity, which is the first antithesis of being and non-being, active energy and passive matter were produced. Later through desire, which is the germ of mind, all further developments took place.

The well-known ancient Hebrew version of the creation asserts that in the beginning the god Jehovah created Earth, but the Earth was without form, and void. Then Jehovah created the firmament, which he called heaven, and ordered the waters under the heaven to be gathered together into one place, and dry lands to appear between the waters. Then the light, which was created earlier, was assigned to the newly created sources such as Sun, Moon, and stars.

It is peculiar that Greek mythology, being very much concerned with the genealogy of the Olympic gods, does not contain a story of creation. The gods, Mount Olympus on which they lived, and the lands above which it rises, were considered as eternal. This point of view can be considered as the precursor of the modern theory of the "steady-state" universe, according to which the universe has existed throughout eternity.*

THE AGE OF THE OCEANS

One way to approach the question of the age of our planet is to ask oneself why the ocean water is so salty. If, as may be true, the Earth was very hot at the time of its formation, all water must

---

* A critical analysis of the steady-state theory can be found in the author's book *The Creation of the Universe* (New York: The Viking Press, revised edition 1961; first published 1952). More recent discussion of this theory can be found in the author's article in *The Great Ideas of Today, 1962*, published by the Encyclopedia Britannica.

have been in the atmosphere in the form of vapor and have come down in the form of torrential rains only after the Earth's surface cooled below the boiling point of water. We know that rainwater carries no salts, so the conclusion seems to be inevitable that when the oceans were first formed they must have been filled with fresh water.

How did salt come to the oceans in such large amounts as we find it today? The answer is that the salinity of ocean water is the result of the work of rivers. Rainwater which falls on the surface of the continents is fresh, but, running down the slopes of mountains and hills, it erodes the surface rocks, washing away minute amounts of salt and carrying them into the ocean. These small concentrations of salt in river water give it a pleasant taste, as can be witnessed by anybody who has tried to drink chemically pure distilled water. Some thousand billion tons of water are evaporated daily from the surface of the oceans heated by the rays of the sun, and the salt that was dissolved in it is left behind in the oceans. Water vapor in the atmosphere condenses into clouds, and a considerable part of it falls back on the continents. Down runs the fresh rainwater again, dissolving more salt on its way back to the ocean. Thus, water moves in an eternal cycle while salt moves only one way, from the continents into the oceans, slowly increasing their salinity.

Knowing the total amount of salt dissolved in ocean water at present, and the amount of salt brought in annually by rivers, one should be able, by simple division, to find out how long rivers must have been operating to bring up the salinity of ocean water from zero to its present value of about three per cent. The figure for the age of oceans obtained this way is, however, rather uncertain. First of all, the rate of erosion during past geological eras may not necessarily have been the same as it is today. In fact, we know that there were long periods of time in the past when continents were mostly flat, the older mountains having been washed away and the new ones not yet formed. During these periods, the rate of erosion must have been considerably slower, and less salt was brought annually by the rivers into the oceans. We also cannot be sure that all the salt brought into the oceans since their formation is still in water solution today. Large bodies of water could have been cut off from the ocean basins (as the Great Salt Lake is today) and gradually evaporated, forming large deposits of rock salt. Because of great uncertainty in these two factors, this method of estimating the age of the oceans can give only approximate results, and any exact figure based on it should be taken with a grain of salt. But, making the most plausible assumptions concerning erosion rates in the past and the amount of salt lost in the formation of solid deposits, one comes to the conclusion that the age of the oceans must be some few billion years.

THE AGE OF ROCKS

A much more precise and reliable method for estimating the age of the Earth is based on the study of radioactive materials found, even though in small amounts, in most of the rocks forming the crust of the Earth. The atoms of radioactive elements such as uranium and thorium are intrinsically unstable and decay slowly into atoms of successively lighter elements, resulting finally in the formation of stable isotopes of lead.

By direct experiment it was discovered that the activity of radioactive material decreases with time, and that the rate of decay differs for the various kinds of radioisotopes. The time required for half of the atoms in a given amount of radioactive material to disintegrate is called its half-life. For example, uranium-238 has a half-life of 4,500,000,000 years and that of thorium-232 is 14,000,000,000 years. It would take twice as long a time to reduce the initial amount of uranium or thorium to one-quarter, and three times as long to reduce it to one-eighth. The end-products of the decay of uranium-238 and of thorium-232 are lead-206 and lead-208, respectively. Thus, for any given rock, the ratio of the amount of parent uranium and thorium still left, to the amount of the lead isotopes produced by their radioactive decay, gives exact information about the time which has passed since the rock was first formed. Indeed, in the molten interior of the Earth, lead produced by the decay of radioactive elements can be separated from the parent substance in the streams of fluid material. Once, however, this material comes to the surface, as the result of volcanic eruptions, and solidifies, the newly produced lead remains at the place of its origin, and its relative amount gives us a clear indication of the number of years which have passed since that rock became solid.

The possibility of telling rather exactly the age of igneous rocks formed at different geological eras of the history of our planet is an invaluable aid to historical geology and paleontology, and can help to determine the absolute chronology of the development of lands, oceans, and ancient life. Because of fossilized remains contained in these rocks, we can tell with certainty that the era of dinosaurs, the giant lizards of the past, was about 150 million years before our time, while the early living forms such as trilobites, resembling today's horseshoe crabs, lived about 500 million years ago.

But farther down are the rocks corresponding to still earlier periods of the Earth's history, which seem to be devoid of any remnants of life. It is very likely that life did exist at the time these rocks were formed, but it must have been limited to the simplest organisms, which left no trace as fossils. The oldest rocks known to us are granites from Rhodesia to which the uranium-lead dating method ascribes the age of 2.7 billion years. But it is almost certain that rocks at still greater depths will show a still greater age. Very interesting information concerning these older rocks may be obtained by drilling a deep hole in the bottom of the ocean — the so-called Project Mohole, which is described in more detail in Chapter 4.

HELP FROM HEAVEN

While it is difficult to get rocks from the deep interior of the Earth, to estimate their age, we get unexpected help from exactly the opposite direction. Stones of various sizes fall on the Earth from interplanetary space and are picked up in large quantities from the ground. These so-called *meteorites* enter our atmosphere in astonishing numbers of about one hundred million per year, with a total weight of about five million tons annually. Most of them are comparatively small, but once in a while they may weigh hundreds of thousands of tons. One meteorite of that size hit the Earth about eight thousand years ago, producing the famous Meteor Crater in Arizona. Another, probably of comparable size, hit Siberia in 1908. The energy developed in these impacts was comparable to that of an H-bomb, and it would be too bad if another should hit one of our big cities. Fortunately these giant cosmic projectiles enter the Earth's atmosphere only rarely. Smaller meteorites are much more abundant, but still not abundant enough to constitute a real danger. It seems that the only recorded case of damage was due to a meteorite about the size of an egg, which went through the roof of the garage of a house in Illinois, broke through the top of a parked car and through its back seat, and bent its exhaust pipe. But the owners of the car were only pleased, since their photographs, along with the parts of their damaged car and the space-stone that hit it, are now on permanent exhibition in the Museum of Natural History in Chicago.

Meteorites are of very great value for science. Their origin is hidden in mystery, but the most probable hypothesis is that they are the fragments of a planet which once moved between the orbits of Mars and Jupiter. As we will see in Chapter 3, a large gap between these two planets is occupied by a belt of asteroids, a swarm of small bodies ranging from several hundred miles in diameter down to the size of pebbles and grains of sand. There are about two thousand asteroids large enough to be seen through a telescope, but there must be millions and billions of smaller ones. The prevailing hypothesis is that a long time ago there must have been a planet, which we may call *Aster*, moving along that orbit. What happened to it we do not know, and probably never will know. Maybe it collided with another planet moving along a nearby orbit; maybe it was hit by some ponderous body coming from outside the solar system; or maybe, as the joke goes, its inhabitants conquered atomic energy, and blew themselves and their planet to pieces. The theory is, however, that fragments resulting from that ancient cosmic catastrophe are now spread along a broad belt between Mars and Jupiter, and some of them, deflected from their circular motion by the forces of gravity exerted by the neighboring planets, have run amok through space and hit anything they encountered on the way.

Meteorites which we pick up are essentially of two kinds: 1) *stony meteorites* composed of substances similar to the rocks forming the crust of the Earth, and 2) *iron meteorites* formed of nickel-iron alloys. This fact agrees very nicely with the hypothesis that meteorites are fragments of a broken-up planet, since, as we shall see later, our Earth and presumably other planets are made of an inner iron core surrounded by a thick rocky mantle. Thus, studying meteorites, we have samples which are representative of all the depths below the surface of the ill-fated Aster. In studies of meteorites by radioactive methods, Claire C. Patterson of the California Institute of Technology found that the average age of meteorites is 4.5 billion years. Since it is reasonable to assume that all planets of the solar system originated at about the same time, the same figure could be accepted as correct for the age of the Earth. Thus, it seems, we have to conclude that the oldest rocks (2.7 billion years old) found on the surface of the Earth were formed when the Earth was about half as old as it is now. Let us hope that this conclusion will be confirmed as we drill deeper down into the body of our planet.

KANT-LAPLACE HYPOTHESIS
VS. COLLISION HYPOTHESIS

In the second half of the eighteenth century the famous German philosopher Immanuel Kant published a book entitled *General Natural History and the Theory of the Heavens,** in which he expressed his views on the origin of the planetary sys-

---

* *Allgemeine Naturgeshichte und Theorie des Himmels.*

tem. According to these views the Sun was originally surrounded by a ring of gaseous material which looked not unlike Saturn's ring. Under the action of the forces of Newtonian gravity between the different parts of the ring, its material condensed into a number of globular bodies which became various planets circling the Sun. A number of years later the no-less-famous French mathematician Pierre Simon de Laplace published a book entitled *A Discussion of the World System,** in which, presumably without knowledge of Kant's publication, he presented essentially the same hypothesis concerning the origin of the planetary system. Neither of the two authors went into any detailed mathematical arguments to support their views, and both books were written in a purely descriptive fashion. This is quite understandable in the case of Kant, who was a professional philosopher, but it is strange that Laplace, who was one of the greatest mathematicians of his time, did not try his hand at explaining the reasons for his theory.

In any case, the Kant-Laplace hypothesis was first subjected to a strict mathematical analysis about a century later by the great British theoretical physicist James Clerk Maxwell. Among the many things which interested Maxwell was the problem of Saturn's ring. By this time it was well known that Saturn's ring† is not a solid disk, resembling a victrola record, but rather a swarm of innumerable bodies ranging in size from a mountain to a sand grain and circling the planet under the forces of Newtonian gravity. Why, Maxwell asked himeslf, don't these particles condense into several individual satellites as a result of the Newtonian gravity forces acting upon them? If, according to the Kant-Laplace hypothesis, the original disk surrounding the Sun condensed into a comparatively small number of individual satellites, why doesn't Saturn's ring do the same?

Maxwell's approach to the problem was based on the fact that

---

* *Exposition du Système du Monde.*

† Saturn's ring is actually composed of three concentric rings with dark spaces between them, but for the purpose of this discussion we may just as well consider it as one ring.

in Saturn's ring, just as in the case of the hypothetical ring surrounding the young Sun, one must consider two kinds of forces acting on the moving bodies forming it. First, of course, there are the forces of mutual gravity which favor condensation. The bodies moving close to one another are pulled together, forming a larger aggregate of matter. Gravitational attraction exerted by this larger aggregation pulls in bodies from longer distances, and so the condensation grows continuously in size and mass.

But there are also other kinds of forces which attempt to break up the rudimentary condensations resulting from the gravity forces. We know that Saturn's ring does not rotate as a single rigid disk, and that the rotation period of its inner rim is shorter than the rotation period of its outer rim. This is a direct consequence of Kepler's third law of planetary motion, which states that the squares of the rotation periods increase as the cubes of the distance from the rotation center. Thus, when a part of the ring begins to condense, the inner part of that condensation runs ahead while the outer part lags behind. As a result, the material forming the condensation is again spread all along the entire circle and the rudimentary condensation is dissolved. Which of the two groups of forces wins the competition depends on their relative strength. The more mass there is in the ring, the stronger is the gravitational attraction between its various parts and the better are the chances that the rudimentary condensation will hold and grow instead of being dissolved. Maxwell applied this criterion to Saturn's ring and found that, indeed, there is not enough mass in it to hold rudimentary condensations together against the disrupting action of varying rotation speeds. So, fine and dandy! Saturn's ring should not be able to condense into individual satellites, and so it doesn't.

The next step was to apply the same considerations to a much larger ring, which, according to the Kant-Laplace hypothesis, surrounded the Sun. Maxwell took the combined mass of all the planets of the solar system, and assumed that it was uniformly distributed in a flat ring around the Sun. He applied his condensation criterion to this hypothetical ring, and came out with the astounding result that it could not possibly have condensed into individual planets. There simply was not enough mass in it for gravitational forces to break it up into individual planets. This result delivered a mortal blow to the Kant-Laplace hypothesis, which had been riding high, wide, and handsome for more than a century.

Theoretical astronomers all over the world started looking for another possibility, and the only other reasonable way in which the planetary system could have been formed was proposed independently by Sir James Jeans in England and F. R. Moulton and T. C. Chamberlin in the United States. This alternative, known as the *collision hypothesis*, assumed that at some time in the distant past our Sun collided with some other star of about equal size. It need not have been a direct collision, but the two celestial bodies must have passed sufficiently close to each other so that the forces of mutual gravity could pull out of their bodies giant tongues of gaseous material which, being joined together, may have formed a temporary bridge between them. As the two stars separated again in their flight through space, the temporary bridge may have broken into a number of globulae, half of them remaining with the Sun and condensing into planets, and the other half being carried away by the other star.

From its very origin the collision hypothesis ran into serious difficulties. The main difficulty was that planets formed in such a collision process should be moving along strongly elongated elliptical trajectories, whereas we know that planetary orbits, though ellipses, deviate only very little from circles. And it was practically impossible to understand how an elongated elliptical orbit could have changed into a nearly circular orbit.

WEIZSÄCKER'S THEORY

The Gordian knot of the theories of planetary origins was finally cut by a young German physicist, Carl von Weizsäcker, in the fall of 1943. Using the new information collected by recent astrophysical research, he was able to show that all the old objections against the Kant-Laplace hypothesis can be easily removed, and that, proceeding along these lines, one can build a detailed theory of the origin of planets, explaining many important features of the planetary system that had not even been touched by any of the old theories.

Weizsäcker was able to accomplish this principally because during the two preceding decades astrophysicists had completely changed their minds about the chemical composition of matter in the universe. Before that time, the chemical elements forming the Sun and all the other stars were generally believed to be present in those bodies in approximately the same proportions in which they occur in the Earth. Geochemical analysis teaches us that the body of the Earth is made up chiefly of oxygen (in the form of various oxides), silicon, aluminum, iron, and smaller quantities of other heavier elements. Light gases such as hydrogen and helium (along with other so-called rare gases such as neon, argon, etc.) are present on the Earth in very small quantities.*

In the absence of any better evidence, astronomers had assumed that these gases were also very rare in the bodies of the Sun and the other stars. However, more detailed theoretical study of stellar structure led the Danish astrophysicist B. Stromgren to the conclusion that such an assumption is quite incorrect, and that, in fact, at least 35 per cent of the material of our Sun must be pure hydrogen. Later this estimate was increased to more than 50 per cent, and it was also found that a considerable percentage of the other solar constituents is pure helium. Both the theoretical studies of the solar interior (which culminated in the important work of M. Schwarzschild), and the more elaborate spectroscopic analysis of its surface, led astrophysicists to a striking conclusion that the common chemical elements that form the body of the Earth constitute only about 1 per cent of the solar mass, the rest being almost evenly divided between hydrogen

---

* Hydrogen is found on our planet mostly in its union with oxygen in water. But everybody knows that although water covers three-quarters of the Earth's surface the total water mass is very small compared with the mass of the entire body of the Earth.

and helium, with a slight preponderance of the former. Apparently this analysis also fits the constitution of the other stars.

Further, it is now known that interstellar space is not quite empty, but is filled by a mixture of gas and fine dust with a mean density of about 1 milligram (.000035 ounce) of matter in 1,000,000 cubic miles of space. This diffuse, highly rarefied material apparently has the same chemical constitution as have the Sun and the other stars.

In spite of its incredibly low density, the presence of this interstellar material can be easily proved, since it produces noticeable selective absorption of light from stars which are so distant that their light has to travel for hundreds of thousands of light-years* through space before entering into our telescopes. The intensity and location of these "interstellar absorption lines" permit us to obtain good estimates of the density of that diffuse material and also to show that it consists almost exclusively of hydrogen and helium. In fact, the dust, formed by small particles about (0.00004 inches in diameter) of various "terrestrial" materials, constitutes not more than 1 per cent of its total mass.

To return to the basic idea of Weizsäcker's theory, we may say that this new knowledge concerning the chemical constitution of matter in the universe plays directly into the hand of the Kant-Laplace hypothesis. In fact, if the primordial gaseous envelope of the Sun was originally formed from such material, only a small portion of it, representing heavier terrestrial elements, could have been used to build our Earth and other planets. The rest of it, represented by noncondensible hydrogen and helium gases, must have been somehow removed, either by falling into the Sun or by being dispersed into surrounding interstellar space. Since the first possibility would have resulted in much more rapid axial rotation of the Sun than it actually has, we have to accept another alternative, namely, that the gaseous "excess material" was dispersed into space soon after the planets were formed from the "terrestrial" compound.

From these facts a new picture of the formation of the plane-

---

* One light-year is approximately 6,000,000,000,000 miles.

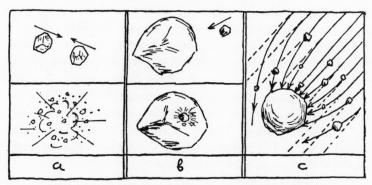

Ill. 1. How the planets would have formed by accretion.

tary system emerges. When the Sun was first formed by the condensation of interstellar matter, a large part of this matter, probably about a hundred times the present combined mass of the planets, remained on the outside, forming a giant rotating envelope. (The reason for such behavior can easily be found in the differences between the rotational states of various interstellar gases which condensed into the primitive Sun.) This rapidly rotating envelope should be visualized as consisting of noncondensible gases (hydrogen, helium, and a smaller amount of other gases) and dust particles of various terrestrial materials (such as iron oxides, silicon compounds, water droplets, and ice crystals) which were floating inside the gas and were carried along by its rotational motion. The formation of big lumps of "terrestrial" material, which we now call planets, must have taken place as the result of collisions between dust particles and their gradual aggregation into larger and larger bodies. Illus. 1 shows the results of such collisions, which must have taken place at velocities comparable to those of meteorites.

One must conclude, on the basis of logical reasoning, that at such velocities the collision of two particles of about equal mass would result in their mutual pulverization (Illus. 1*a*), a process leading not to the growth of larger lumps of matter but to the destruction of the colliding particles. On the other hand, when a small particle collided with a much larger one (Illus. 1*b*), it seems evident that the smaller one would bury itself in the body of the larger, thus forming a new, somewhat larger mass.

Obviously these two processes would result in the gradual disappearance of smaller particles and the aggregation of their material into larger bodies. In the later stages the process will be accelerated because the larger lumps of matter will attract gravitationally the smaller particles passing by and add them to their own growing bodies. This is illustrated in Illus. 1c, which shows how, as the process continues, massive lumps of matter become increasingly effective in capturing smaller ones.

Weizsäcker was able to show that the fine dust originally scattered through the entire region now occupied by the planetary system must have been aggregated into a few big lumps to form the planets, within a period of about 100,000,000 years.

As long as the planets were growing by the accretion of variously sized pieces of cosmic matter on their way around the Sun, the constant bombardment of their surfaces by fresh building material must have kept their bodies very hot. However, as soon as the supply of stellar dust, pebbles, and larger rocks was exhausted, thus stopping the process of growth, radiation into interstellar space must have rapidly cooled the outer layers of the newly formed celestial bodies, leading to the formation of a solid crust, which goes on getting thicker as slow internal cooling continues.

PLANETARY DISTANCE

The next important point which any theory of planetary origin must explain is the peculiar rule (known as the Titus-Bode rule) that governs the distances of different planets from the sun. The table on page 15 shows these distances for the nine planets* of the solar system, as well as for the belt of asteroids. The figures in the last column are of especial interest. In spite of some varia-

---

* The ninth planet, Pluto, is believed to be of more recent origin, being an escaped satellite of Neptune (see Chapter 3).

DISTANCE OF PLANETS FROM THE SUN

Planet	Distance from the Sun (in terms of Earth's distance from the Sun)	Ratio of the distance from the Sun of each planet to that of the planet listed above it
Mercury	0.387	
Venus	0.723	1:86
Earth	1.000	1.38
Mars	1.524	1.52
Asteroids	about 2.7	1.77
Jupiter	5.203	1.92
Saturn	9.539	1.83
Uranus	19.191	2.001
Neptune	30.07	1.56
Pluto	39.52	1.31

tions, it is evident that none are very far from the numeral 2, which permits us to formulate the approximate rule: *The radius of each planetary orbit is roughly twice as large as that of the orbit nearest it in the direction of the Sun.*

It is interesting to notice that a similar rule holds also for the satellites of individual planets, a fact that can be demonstrated by the table below, which gives the relative distances of the nine recognized satellites of Saturn.

As in the case of the planets themselves, there are quite large deviations (especially for Phoebe!), but there is little doubt that there is a definite trend toward the same type of regularity.

DISTANCE OF SATURN'S SATELLITES FROM THE PLANET

Satellite	Distance from Saturn in terms of Saturn's radius	Ratio of increase in two successive distances
Mimas	3.11	
Enceladus	3.99	1.28
Tethys	4.94	1.24
Dione	6.33	1.28
Rhea	8.84	1.39
Titan	20.48	2.31
Hyperion	24.82	1.21
Japetus	59.68	2.40
Phoebe	216.8	3.63

How can we explain the fact that the aggregation process that took place in the original dust cloud surrounding the Sun did not result in the first place in just one big planet, and the reason the several big lumps were formed at these particular distances from the Sun?

To answer this question we have to undertake a somewhat more detailed survey of the motions that took place in the original dust cloud. We must remember first of all that every material body — whether it is a tiny dust particle, a small meteorite, or a big planet — that moves around the Sun is bound, under the Newtonian law of attraction, to describe an elliptical orbit with the Sun at its focus. If the material forming the planets was formerly in the form of separate particles, say, 0.00004 inches in diameter,* there must have been some 10^{45} particles moving along elliptical orbits of all sorts of sizes and elongations. It is clear that in such heavy traffic numerous collisions must have taken place between the individual particles, and that, as the result of such collisions, the motion of the entire swarm must have become to a certain extent organized. In fact, it is not difficult to understand that such collisions served either to pulverize the "traffic violators" or to force them to "detour" into less crowded "traffic lanes." What are the laws that would govern such organized or at least partially organized traffic?

To make the first approach to the problem, let us select a group of particles all of which had the same rotation period around the Sun. Some of these were moving along a circular orbit of a corresponding radius, whereas others were describing various more or less elongated elliptical orbits (Illus. 2a). Let us now try to describe the motion of these various particles from the point of view of coordinate system X–Y rotating around the center of the Sun with the same period as the particles (Illus. 2b).

First of all, from the point of view of such a rotating coordinate system, the particle A that was moving along a circular orbit would appear to be completely at rest at a certain point A'. A particle B that was moving around the Sun following an elliptical

---

* The approximate size of the dust particles forming the interstellar material.

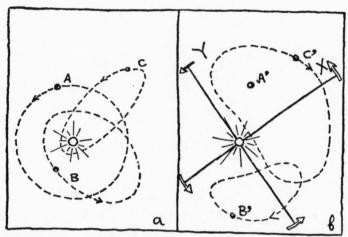

Ill. 2. Circular and elliptic motion as viewed from (*a*) a resting coordinate
system, and (*b*) a rotating one.

trajectory comes closer to and farther away from the Sun, and its
angular velocity around the center is larger in the first case and
smaller in the second; thus, it will sometimes run ahead of the
uniformly rotating coordinate system X–Y and sometimes will lag
behind. It is not difficult to see that, from the point of view of
this system, the particle will be found to describe a closed bean-
shaped trajectory marked B' in Illus. 2*b*. Still another particle
C, which was moving along a more elongated ellipse, will be
seen in the system X–Y as describing a similar but somewhat
larger bean-shaped trajectory C'.

It is clear now that, if we want to arrange the motion of the
entire swarm of particles so that they never collide with one
another, it must be done in such a way that the bean-shaped
trajectories described by these particles in the uniformly rotating
coordinate system X–Y do not intersect.

Remembering that the particles having common rotation periods around the Sun keep the same average distance from it, we
find that the nonintersecting pattern of their trajectories in the
system X–Y must look like a "bean necklace" surrounding the Sun.

The aim of the preceding analysis, which may be a bit too

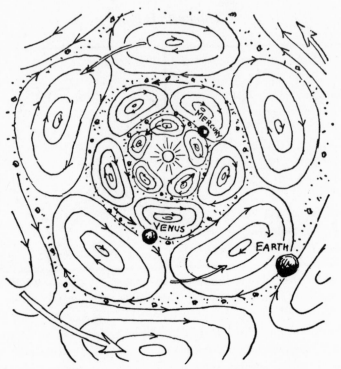

Ill. 3. "Traffic lanes" of the dust in the original solar envelope.

hard on the reader but which represents in principle a fairly simple procedure, is to show the nonintersecting traffic pattern for individual groups of particles moving at the same mean distance from the Sun and possessing therefore the same period of rotation. Since among the original dust particles surrounding the primitive Sun we should expect to encounter all different mean distances, and correspondingly all different rotation periods, the actual situation must have been more complicated. Instead of just one "bean necklace" there must have been a large number of such "necklaces" rotating in respect to one another with various speeds. By careful analysis of the situation, Weizsäcker was able to show that for the stability of such a system it is necessary that each separate "necklace" should contain five separate whirlpool systems, so that the entire picture of motion must have looked very much like Illus. 3. Such an arrangement would assure "safe traffic" within each individual ring, but since these rings rotated with different periods, there must have been "traffic accidents" where one ring touched another. The large number of mutual collisions taking place in these boundary regions between the particles belonging to one ring and those belonging to neighboring rings must have been responsible for the aggregation process, and for the growth of larger and larger lumps of matter at these particular distances from the sun. Thus, through a gradual thinning process within each ring, and through the accumulation of matter at the boundary regions between them, the planets were finally formed.

This picture of the formation of the planetary system gives us a simple explanation of the rule governing the radii of planetary orbits. In fact, simple geometrical considerations show that in a pattern of the type shown in Illus. 3, the radii of successive boundary lines between the neighboring rings form a simple geometrical progression, each being twice as large as the previous one. We also see why this rule cannot be expected to be quite exact. In fact it is not the result of a strict law governing the motion of particles in the original dust cloud but must be considered rather as expressing a certain tendency in the otherwise irregular process of dust traffic.

The fact that the same rule also holds for the satellites of different planets of our system indicates that the process of satellite formation took place roughly along the same lines. When the original dust cloud surrounding the Sun was broken up into the separate groups of particles that were to form the individual planets, the process repeated itself in each case with most of the material concentrating in the center to form the body of the planet, and the rest of it circling around and condensing gradually into a number of satellites. The formation of the Earth's satellite, the Moon, may be an exceptional case, which is discussed in Chapter 2.

With all this discussion of mutual collisions and the growth of dust particles, we have forgotten to tell what happened to the gaseous part of the primordial solar envelope, which, as may be remembered, constituted originally about 99 per cent of its en-

Ill. 4. After the Sun attained its full brightness, the pressure of its radiation drove the hydrogen-helium envelopes of the protoplanets into space, revealing their solid cores. In this drawing no attention was given to geometrical dimensions, as it was intended to pertain to any of the billions of planetary systems within the Milky Way.

tire mass. The answer to this question is a comparatively simple one.

While the dust particles were colliding, forming larger and larger lumps of matter, the gases that were unable to participate in that process were gradually dissipating into interstellar space. It can be shown by comparatively simple calculations that the time necessary for such dissipation was about 100,000,000 years, which is about the same as the period of planetary growth. Thus, by the time the planets were finally formed, most of the hydrogen and helium that had formed the original solar envelope must have escaped from the solar system, leaving only negligibly small traces which are known as the Zodiacal Light.

Weizsäcker's theory of the origin of the planetary system was later modified by the Dutch-born American astronomer Gerald Kuiper. According to his views, the condensation of the nebulous ring surrounding the primordial Sun took place faster than the condensation of the Sun itself. Thus the planets must have been born in darkness before the energy-producing mechanism of the Sun went into action. Under such circumstances the hydrogen and helium gases of the original ring must have been retained by the condensing dust particles, forming extensive planetary atmospheres hundreds of times heavier than the planets themselves. These *protoplanets*, as Kuiper calls them, rotated around the slowly condensing Sun until nuclear reactions started in the interior of the Sun, which then began to pour intensive radiation into the surrounding space. When the Sun became luminous the light-pressure of its radiation began to blow the gaseous atmospheres of the protoplanets out of the solar system, and for a while protoplanets looked like giant comets with bushy tails of escaping hydrogen and helium gases. In the case of Mercury, Venus, the Earth, and Mars, which are nearest to the Sun, the dissipation of primordial gaseous atmospheres was completed, and we are walking now on the surface of a solid rocky sphere which was once a kernel of one of the protoplanets. In the case of Jupiter, Saturn, and other planets located farther away from the Sun, only a part of the primary hydrogen-helium atmosphere was blown away, while the rest of it was retained by the gravity forces of the central solid kernel. The presence of extensive gaseous atmosphere on the outer planets accounts for the fact that their mean densities, calculated from the observed diameters and masses, are considerably lower than the mean densities of inner planets such as our Earth.

Planet	Mean Density	Planet	Mean Density
Mercury	3.8	Jupiter	1.3
Venus	4.9	Saturn	0.7
Earth	5.5	Uranus	1.3
Mars	4.0	Neptune	1.6

PLURALITY OF INHABITABLE WORLDS

One important consequence of the Weizsäcker theory lies in the conclusion that the formation of the planetary system was not an exceptional event, but one that must have taken place in the formation of practically all the stars. This statement stands in sharp contrast with the conclusions of the collision theory, which considered the process by which the planets were formed as very exceptional in cosmic history. In fact, the stellar collisions that were supposed to give rise to planetary systems were regarded as extremely rare events, and among 40,000,000,000 stars forming our stellar system of the Milky Way, only a few such collisions were believed to have taken place during several billion years of its existence.

If, as it appears now, each star possesses a system of planets, there must be, within our galaxy alone, millions of planets the physical conditions on which are almost identical with those on our Earth. And it would be at least strange if life — even in its highest forms — had failed to develop in these "inhabitable" worlds.

In fact, the simplest forms of life, such as different kinds of viruses, actually are merely rather complicated molecules composed mainly of carbon, hydrogen, oxygen, and nitrogen atoms. Since these elements must be present in sufficient abundance on the surface of any newly formed planet, we must believe that sooner or later after the formation of a solid crust and the precipitation of atmospheric vapors forming the extensive water reservoirs, a few molecules of such type must have appeared, owing to an accidental combination of the necessary atoms in the necessary order. To be sure, the complexity of living molecules makes the probability of their accidental formation extremely small, and we can compare it with the probability of putting together a jigsaw puzzle by simply shaking the separate pieces in their box with the hope that they will accidentally arrange themselves in the proper way. But on the other hand we must not forget that there were an immense number of atoms continuously colliding with one another, and also a lot of time in which to achieve the necessary result. The fact that life appeared on our Earth rather soon after the formation of the crust indicates that, improbable as it seems, the accidental formation of a complex organic molecule required probably only a few hundred million years. Once the simplest forms of life appeared on the surface of the newly formed planet, the process of organic reproduction, and the gradual process of evolution, would lead to the formation of more and more complicated forms of living organisms. There is no telling whether the evolution of life on different "inhabitable" planets takes the same track as it did on our Earth. The study of life in different worlds would contribute essentially to our understanding of the evolutionary process.

But whereas we may be able to study the forms of life that may have developed on Mars and Venus (the best "inhabitable" planets of the solar system) in the not too distant future by means of a trip to these planets by space ship, the question about the possible existence of life and the forms it may take in other stellar worlds may remain forever an unsolvable problem of science.

Of course one can say that with the future development of rocket technology we will sometime be able to visit other stars and get acquainted with the inhabitants of the distant planetary systems. There is, however, a strong argument against such a probability, brought forward by the late Enrico Fermi. If life exists on the billions of inhabitable planets within the stellar system of the Milky Way, we should expect it to be in various stages of evolutionary development, since the rate of evolution must depend on particular physical conditions existing in these distant worlds. A difference of a few percentage points in the rate of evolution would result in millions of years' difference in the degree of development of life in the distant inhabitable worlds. Thus on some of the planetary systems scattered through the Milky Way, life may be still in the pre-mammalian stage, while on the others intelligent beings similar to ourselves may have been developed millions of years ago and have reached by now much higher perfection in science and technology than we. Therefore it would seem that if interstellar spaceship communications were at all possible, the inhabitants of these advanced worlds should have come to visit us on the Earth. The fact that we do not have any visitors from outer space (except for flying saucers, which are pure hokum) indicates that we, the people of the Earth, will never be able to travel to the stars.

There is, however, another possibility for discovering the existence of superior intellectual beings who may inhabit other worlds. They may have developed powerful interstellar radio communication stations, and if so, our radiotelescopes registering the radio noise originating in distant stars and stellar galaxies may pick up radio signals resembling the Morse Code, which cannot originate in a natural way and will have to be ascribed to the work of intelligent beings. So far, however, nothing of that kind has been noticed in the cosmic radio waves arriving at the Earth.

2

Our Faithful Moon

OCEAN TIDES

ALONG WITH its well-known romantic value, and a number of legends and superstitions connected with it, the Moon is responsible for the phenomenon of the ocean tides. Twice a day the surface of the ocean rises up a few feet and then falls back again. Along the open coastlines high and low tides result in alternating expansion and shrinkage of beach areas and the periodic submergence and exposure of rocks just off the shore. But in special cases, when the rising tide enters narrow fiords or river estuaries, events may become considerably more violent. Thus, for example, the rising waters of the Atlantic Ocean which are squeezed into the estuary of the Amazon River present one of the most magnificent examples of the blind forces of nature.

As was first explained by Isaac Newton, founder of the theory of universal gravity, tides are due to the gravitational forces of the Moon and the Sun acting on the ocean waters. Although the Sun is much more massive than the Moon, it is so much farther away that its tide-producing force is about four times smaller than that of the Moon. When the Sun and the Moon are on the same line with the Earth, i.e., during the new moon and full moon periods, they both pull ocean waters together and the resulting tides are higher. On the other hand, during the first and the last quarter, when the Moon looks like a semicircle, its action on the ocean waters is in the opposite direction to that of the Sun and the resulting tides are lower.

At first glance it seems hard to understand why there are two high tides daily. If the Moon attracts ocean waters, the ocean level, so it seems, should rise on the Earth's side turned toward the Moon, and fall on the opposite side. Why, instead of doing that, do the ocean waters bulge up *on both sides?* The explanation of that seemingly paradoxical phenomenon is based on the fact that we deal here with the relative motion of the Moon and the Earth, both of them being free in space. If the Moon were fixed on the top of some giant steel tower erected on one of the Earth's continents, there would be a permanent high tide in that hemisphere, and a permanent low tide in the opposite one. But, since both celestial bodies are free to move in space, they both revolve around the common center of gravity which (because of much larger mass of the Earth) is located close to the Earth's center. In fact, the center of the revolution of both the Moon and the Earth is located within the body of the Earth at about three-quarters of the distance from its center to its surface (Illus. 5).

Since the Earth moves around that center just as the Moon does, the situation becomes dynamic rather than static as it would have been if the Moon were sitting on the top of a tower. To find out what happens in this case, we must consider the gravity forces of the Moon acting on: 1) ocean waters facing the Moon; 2) the solid body of the Earth; and 3) the ocean waters on the opposite side. Since gravity forces decrease with the distance, they will be largest in case 1, smaller in case 2, and still smaller in case 3. Therefore the gravitational displacement of ocean waters on the front side caused by the Moon's gravity will be larger than gravitational displacement of the solid globe, so that the ocean level will rise above the ocean floor. By the same token, however, the Earth globe will be displaced toward the Moon more than the ocean waters on the opposite side, so that the ocean floor on that side will be, so to speak, pulled down from under the ocean surface. In the terms of relative motion, it means, of course, that on the opposite side the ocean surface will also rise above the ocean floor.

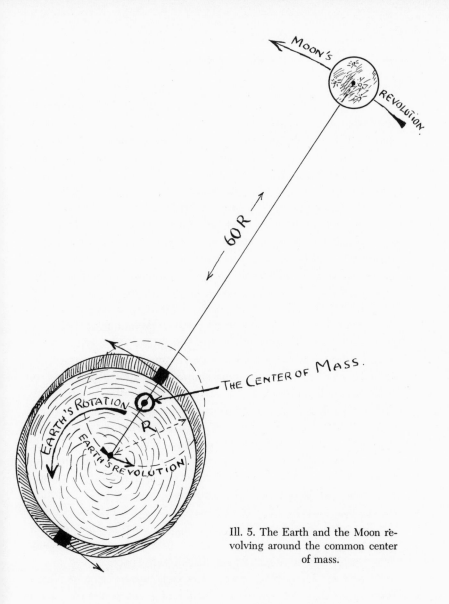

Ill. 5. The Earth and the Moon revolving around the common center
of mass.

THE TIDES IN ROCKS

The effect of tidal forces is not confined to the periodic disturbances of the liquid envelope of our planet alone; the Earth's
rocky body itself is being periodically pushed and pulled by the

uneven attraction acting on its opposite flanks. Since the body of the Earth is certainly less deformable than its liquid envelope, the "tides in rocks" must be smaller than the tides in the oceans, and the rise and fall of the water level that we observe at the seashore must result from the difference between the heights of the two tides. Although we can easily measure this difference, the determination of the separate heights of the two tides is very difficult. In fact, since the tidal deformations of the Earth result in the periodic rise and fall of the entire surface surrounding the observer, the tides in rocks cannot be noticed by an observer on the ground, just as the ocean tides cannot be observed from a boat on the open ocean. One way to estimate the height of the body tides in the Earth would be to calculate the expected height of oceanic tides on the basis of Newton's law and to compare this value with the observed relative elevations of the ocean and land levels. Unfortunately, the theoretical calculation of the ocean tides, which would be very simple if the Earth were a smooth, regular sphere, becomes impossibly difficult because we must take into account all the irregularities of the ocean shores and the varying depths of the ocean basins.

This difficulty was solved in a very ingenious way by the American physicist Albert A. Michelson, who proposed to study the "microtides" raised by solar and lunar attraction in comparatively small bodies of water. His apparatus consisted of a carefully levelled iron pipe, about 500 feet long, which was half filled with water. Under the action of the gravity forces due to the Sun and the Moon, the water surface in this pipe behaves exactly in the same way as the water in the oceans, periodically changing its inclination to a fixed direction in space.

Since this *"Michelson's ocean"* has considerably smaller linear dimensions than, let us say, the Pacific (500 feet as against 10,000 miles), the same inclination of the surface will cause only very small vertical displacements of the water level at the opposite ends of the pipe, so small in fact that they cannot be noticed with the naked eye. Using a sensitive optical device, Michelson was able to observe these small variations of the water level, which amounted to only 0.00002 inches at their maximum. In spite of the small size of these "microtides," he was able to observe all the phenomena familiar on a large scale in the ocean basins of our planet, such as the exceptionally high tides during new moon periods.

Comparing the observed height of the tides in his "micro-ocean" with the theoretical values, which can be easily calculated for this simple case, Michelson noticed that they account for only 69 per cent of the expected effect. *The remaining 31 per cent was evidently compensated for by the tidal dislocation of the Earth's solid surface* on which Michelson's tube was installed. Thus he came to the conclusion that *the observed ocean tides must represent only 69 per cent of the total rise of waters,* and that, since the tides in open oceans are about 2.5 feet high,* *the total rise of water must be about 3.6 feet.*

The remaining 1.1 feet of this total water tide are evidently compensated for by the corresponding up-and-down motion of the rigid crust of the Earth, leaving only the difference of 2.5 feet apparent to observers on the seashore. *Thus, strange as it seems, the ground under our feet is periodically moving up and down with all the cities, hills, and mountains on its surface.* It is pulled up every night when the Moon is high in the sky, and sinks down again as soon as the Moon drops beneath the horizon. The second upward motion occurs when the Moon is directly under our feet and, so to speak, pulls the entire globe down from under us. It goes without saying that this up-and-down motion proceeds so smoothly that it cannot be directly detected by even the most sensitive physical apparatus. The observed fact that the tides in rocks are about four times smaller than the tides in water indicates a comparatively high rigidity of our globe, and, using the theory of elasticity, one can calculate from these data the rigidity of the Earth as a whole. By so doing, the famous English physicist Lord Kelvin was the first to arrive at the conclusion that *the rigidity of the Earth's body is as high as if it were made of good steel.*

---

* The values were observed from an isolated Pacific island which was too small to affect the motion of oceanic waters appreciably.

TIDES ON THE MOON

Just as the gravitational attraction of the Moon produces tides in the oceans and the body of the Earth, the gravitational attraction of the Earth might be expected to produce tides on the Moon. Since there are no oceans on the Moon, these tides must be limited to its solid body. Moreover, since the Moon always faces the Earth with one of its sides, one would expect the tidal deformation of the Moon to be stationary in respect to its body.

Since tidal force is proportional to the mass of the disturbing body, the tides on the Moon, if it were completely liquid and deformable, should have the height of about 150 feet. Detailed study of the shape of the Moon shows that it is in fact elongated in the direction of the Earth, but that elongation is about *thirty times larger* than would be expected for the present distance between the Earth and the Moon. This fact strongly suggests that the observed tidal deformation of the Moon corresponds to the time when the Moon was much closer to the Earth than it is now. At that stage of development the body of the Moon evidently had become too rigid to permit further deformation; the tidal wave became "frozen" and remained unchanged ever after, although, because of the increased distance of the Moon, the forces responsible for the tides were considerably reduced. The presence of this "frozen tide" is evidence of the Moon's extremely high rigidity compared with our Earth, where deformations of the solid crust are constantly taking place even now.

It seems certain, therefore, that *the crust of the Moon is much thicker than that of the Earth, and our satellite is probably solid all the way to its center.* This result can be easily understood, for the Moon must have cooled down considerably faster than our Earth because of its smaller mass.

It is well known that the Moon has no water, but if its surface were half covered by oceans, its geography would represent a very peculiar sight — an almost circular continent, formed by the frozen tidal wave, right in the middle of the disk, with another antipodal continent of the same shape on the opposite side

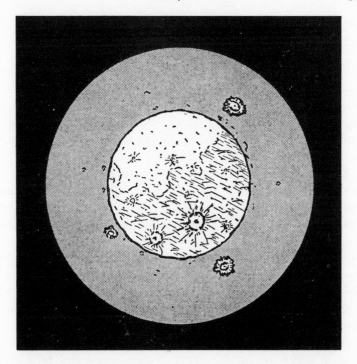

Ill. 6. If there were water on the surface of the Moon, we might see something like this. The bright circle in the center would be one of the two lunar continents.

(Illus. 6). The oceans would be rather shallow, reaching a maximum depth of some 2500 feet at the visible rim of the Moon, while the continents would rise slowly from the shoreline to a high point of about 2500 feet above sea level at their midpoints. Since water has less reflective power than ordinary rock, we should see the brightly illuminated surface of the continent at the center of the Moon surrounded by a considerably darker ring of water. Schoolboys, who rack their brains trying to remember all the seas, bays, peninsulas, and straits on the complicated face of our Earth, would just love such geography!

TIDES AND AGES

Tides and Ages is the title of a book published late in the last century by the British astronomer George Darwin, the son of the famous biologist Charles Darwin. In that book Darwin discusses the question of what effect the tides could have had on the motion of the Earth and the Moon during the time span of billions of years which covers the geological history of our planet.

Let us look at the Earth-Moon system from the outside, for example from Mars. We will observe that the Earth rotates around its axis within a period of 24 hours, while the Moon moves around it, making one revolution in the course of a month or, more exactly, 29½ days. Two tidal bulges on the Earth's oceans point steadily toward and away from the Moon, while the Earth rotates within them much as a wheel rotates between the brakeshoes. The concept of brakes in the previous sentence has more than a casual significance. Indeed, the tidal waves running diurnally around the Earth *do* exert some braking action on its rotation around the axis. The internal friction of water, the friction of water against the ocean bottom (especially in shallow places), and the impacts of tidal waves against the continents standing in their way, dissipate a considerable amount of energy which results in the slowing down of the Earth's axial rotation. Thus each day is a little longer than the previous one, and, in fact, it was found by exact astronomical measurements that each day is 0.00000002 seconds longer than the one before. Small as it is, the effect is cumulative and in the course of many years astronomical timetables would eventually reveal the accumulated error.

Exact astronomical observations over a period of a century show this lengthening quite clearly. If each day is one two-hundred millionth (0.00000002) of a second longer than the previous one, one hundred years (i.e., 36,525 days) ago the length of a day was shorter by 0.00073 seconds. Thus, on the average between then and now, the length of the day was ½ × 0.00073 = 0.00036 seconds shorter than at present. But, since

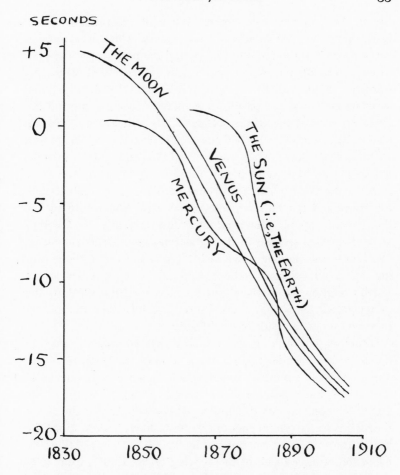

Ill. 7. Time discrepancy between the observed and predicted motion of various celestial bodies. The fact that the four curves are not identical (as they should be if the discrepancy is caused by the slowing of the Earth's rotation) is probably due to small errors in observations and theoretical calculations.

36,525 days have passed by, the total accumulated error must be 36,525 × 0.00036, i.e., 13 seconds.

Thirteen seconds per century is a small figure, but it is well within the range of accuracy of astronomical observations and calculations. In fact, this slowing down of the rotation of the Earth about its axis explains a discrepancy which had puzzled astronomers for a long time. Comparing the positions of the Sun, Moon, Mercury, and Venus in respect to the "fixed" stars, astronomers noticed that they seemed systematically *ahead of time* as compared with the position calculated a century ago on the basis of celestial mechanics (Illus. 7). If a television program started fifteen minutes earlier than you expected it to start, if you found a store closed when you arrived, less than fifteen minutes before closing time, and if you missed a train when you were sure you would catch it, you would not blame the radio station, the shop, and the railroad, but your watch. You would realize that it was probably fifteen minutes slow. Similarly, the discrepancy of thirteen seconds in timing astronomical events should be ascribed to the slowing down of the Earth and not to the speeding up of all celestial bodies. Until the slowing down of the Earth's rotation was realized, astronomers used the Earth as the perfect clock. Now they know better and introduce the correction required as a result of tidal friction.

If the rotation of the Earth around its axis is gradually slowing down because of tidal friction, the motion of the Moon revolving around the Earth must be speeding up. This is a consequence of one of the basic laws of Newtonian mechanics known as *the law of the conservation of angular momentum*. And, if the Moon speeds up in its orbital motion, it must slowly recede from the Earth, moving along an unwinding spiral trajectory (Illus. 8). From the observed rate of the slowing of the Earth's axial rotation one can find out the rate of the Moon's recession from the Earth. And the result is that each time we see the new Moon it is 4 inches farther away from us. Of course, 4 inches per month is not a large distance, considering that the mean distance to the Moon is 238,857 miles. But here again we are interested in the effect of that recession over very long periods of geological time. If the Moon recedes from the Earth, even though very slowly, it must have been much closer to us in some distant past. George Darwin calculated, in fact, that about four and a half billion years ago the Moon must have been almost touching the Earth's

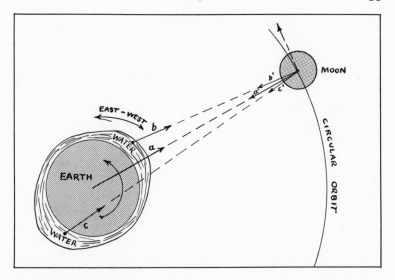

Ill. 8. Forces that slow down the rotation of the Earth and push the Moon farther away.

surface in its orbital motion. Furthermore, he had shown that at that time the length of a day (i.e., the rotation period of the Earth) was only 5 hours, and that at the same time the revolution period of the Moon (i.e., the length of a month) was 5 hours too. Thus, looking four and a half billion years back, we find the Moon revolving around the Earth at a height comparable to that at which today's artificial satellites fly. The great difference is, however, that in those days the Earth was spinning much faster around its axis, and had therefore a much more strongly expressed ellipsoidal shape.

Thus, asked George Darwin, why can't we assume that just before that time the Earth and the Moon had consisted of one single body which broke up into two pieces, the bigger one forming the Earth and the smaller one the Moon? If that was really so, the primary body which experienced the fission can rightfully be called either "Earthoon" or "Moorth." What forces could have accounted for such a breakup? If the Moon was a part of the Earth there were, of course, no lunar tides. But the

young semi-molten body of Earthoon (or Moorth) was subjected to the periodic action of solar tides, which lifted and de-
pressed the surface twice every 5 hours. An exciting point of
Darwin's theory is that the period of these tidal deformations,
i.e., 2½ hours, coincided with the proper oscillation period of
the body. In fact, if two giant hands were to grab the original
Moorth (or Earthoon) and squeeze or stretch it, it would pulsate
for a while with that very period.

When we "tune" our radio or television set to a desired station,
we rotate the knob which changes the oscillation period of the
electronic system enclosed in the case. When that vibration
period becomes equal to the vibration period of the incoming
radio waves (so many kilocycles or megacycles) the reception
system is in *resonance* with the incoming electromagnetic waves
from which it obtains the energy that is transformed into sound
or a picture on the fluorescent screen. A more old-fashioned example is presented by a nurse pushing a child on a swing. In
order to make the swing go higher and faster, she must push it
with the same rhythm as it would swing in if left alone. Similarly,
the periodic tidal force of the Sun's gravity, acting on Earthoon
(or Moorth) at the time intervals corresponding to its own pulsations, would lead to resonance. The pulsations would become
stronger and stronger, and, at a certain point, the original body
might break up into the Earth and the Moon.

PROS AND CONS

The beauty of George Darwin's theory lies in the fact that,
looking back in time on the history of our satellite, we find it
close to the Earth exactly at the time usually ascribed to the
formation of the Earth and planetary system in general, revolving
with exactly the same period as the Earth rotated at that time.
If the tidal forces in the Earth's oceans were different or if the
Earth's rotation period today were not 24 hours, these coincidences would not exist. Of course it is dangerous to base scientific
theories on numerical coincidences, but the existence of such

coincidences does increase our conviction that the theory is correct. Besides, there are other points which independently support Darwin's view. The mean density of the Earth (obtained by simple division of its mass by its volume) is 5.5 larger than the density of water. On the other hand the density of surface rocks is much smaller: 2.6 for granite and 2.8 for basalt. Thus the conclusion is inevitable that the core of the Earth is made of some material with a density considerably higher than 5.5, and it is now generally assumed that our Earth possesses a heavy iron core. The mean density of the Moon is only 3.3, which is consistent with the assumption that it is made all of rocks, which are compressed to somewhat higher density in its central regions. The absence of iron as a constituent of the Moon could be explained if, following Darwin, we assume that it was formed from the outer layers of the original composite body.

Another point in support of Darwin's view is the fact that the surface of the Earth is divided into large continental massives and deep ocean basins. Continents are mainly large slabs of granite averaging about 20 miles in depth, and basalt rocks appear on their surfaces only in patches as a result of volcanic eruptions. Below the depth of 20 miles there is a layer of much heavier material, basalt, on which the continental massives rest. The ocean floors, on the other hand, have no granite at all, being formed entirely of basalt rocks.

As we shall see in Chapter 4, the body of the Earth has an onion-like structure, consisting of a sequence of concentric shells which are composed of successively denser materials toward the core. This distribution would be expected if one assumes that our globe was originally in a molten state, so that heavier material sank to the center and lighter material floated toward the surface. It would seem natural, in that case, that the lighter, granite material would be distributed as a uniform thin shell all over the surface of the globe. Why then do we find granite only in the form of thick slabs covering only about one-quarter of the entire surface? This question can be answered if one assumes that the original Earthoon (or Moorth) had a continuous granite surface layer, which, being exposed to the cold of the surrounding space, became solid rather early. When the Moon separated from the Earth, much of the surface material on one side was taken away, forming a large area (corresponding to the Pacific Ocean) deprived of granite, but a part of the original granite surface was left on the opposite side. The leftover granite layer may have cracked into several pieces which floated somewhat apart, moving across the surface of the still molten basalt. When the upper layers of basalt solidified, the granite slabs were frozen into fixed positions, forming the continents as we know them today. We shall return to this problem in Chapter 5.

But, aside from these supporting arguments, there are also many serious objections to George Darwin's theory. About a hundred years ago the French astronomer M. Roche proved that any satellite which revolves around a planet at a distance less than 2.5 times the planet's radius will be broken to pieces by its gravitation forces.* A good example of the Roche limit is presented by Saturn's satellites and its system of rings. The nearest satellite, called Mimas, revolves around Saturn at a distance of 3.1 times the planet's radius and stays in one piece. On the other hand, the outer radius of the ring system is 2.3 times the radius of the planet and the rings remain in a broken-up state, as a swarm of small particles.

It is argued by the opponents of Darwin's theory that, if the Moon separated from the original body, it would have broken to pieces before it had a chance to escape beyond the Roche limit. However, one can criticize that criticism by saying that, when the Earth was rotating in a 5-hour period, its equatorial diameter was considerably larger than it is today, and the piece which broke away was already beyond the danger zone. The trouble with trying to make a definite decision, either positive or negative, on this problem is that it involves immensely complicated mathematics. The calculations which can be carried out for the solution are only very approximate and their results very indecisive. The only way of making sure whether Darwin's

---

* Artificial satellites which fly today within the Roche limit do not break to pieces because, being built of metal, they are much sturdier than natural satellites.

view is right or wrong is to give the problem to one of the high-speed electronic computers that is capable of following in detail all the intricacies of the separation process. Let us hope that this will be done soon.

Those who choose not to believe Darwin's theory, and among them are such great scientists as Harold Urey, the discoverer of heavy hydrogen and Nobel Prize winner in chemistry, prefer the assumption that the Moon is a body which for some reason failed to join other material which formed the Earth. The condensation of planets from the original cloud around the Sun must have proceeded at a very slow rate, taking hundreds of millions of years for completion. During that time small dust particles floating in the cloud collided with one another and stuck together to form somewhat bigger pieces of solid matter. These pieces continued to grow still larger and larger, reaching the size of a watermelon, of St. Paul's dome, of — Everest. There was an era, according to Urey, when there were thousands of moon-sized bodies revolving at various distances around the Sun. Many of these bodies, moving along orbits close to the present orbit of the Earth, stuck together, forming our globe, but one of them missed the boat and was captured by the Earth as a permanent satellite. Urey's proposal is comparatively new, and a number of years must pass before it can be critically evaluated.

THE MOON'S LANDSCAPE

To the naked eye, the surface of our satellite appears as a patchwork of brighter and darker areas which form the face of the "man in the moon." The first person who was to see the Moon better than that was the famous Italian scientist Galileo Galilei. One day, early in the seventeenth century, Galileo learned that a Dutch spectacle-maker named Hans Lippershey had constructed an amusing gadget consisting of a combination of lenses in a tube. It was said to make distant objects seem very close, so that a tree or a man one or two miles away could be seen clearly. It occurred to Galileo that such a "magic tube," as it was

Ill. 9. Photograph of the full Moon, showing the darker areas ("maria") and the lunar craters, with "light rays" diverging from some of the latter.
(Courtesy of the Yerkes Observatory)

called at that time, could be very helpful for astronomical observation.

The first astronomical telescope which Galileo built with his own hands was a crude affair, but, even so, it permitted him to see the surface of the Moon in much more detail than he had previously. He was the first man to see mountain ridges and large circular craters on the Moon. Through his primitive telescope the large dark areas on the Moon appeared smooth and featureless, as would large bodies of water. Thus he called them *maria*, which is Latin for "seas." This name is still retained, although better telescopes have revealed long since that the alleged "lunar seas" are actually large level plains covered with numerous surface irregularities and splattered all over with a large number of small craters. In fact we are now perfectly cer-

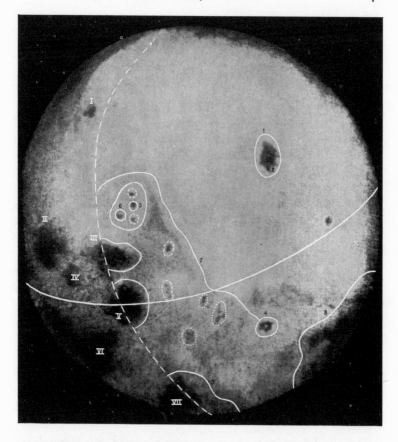

Ill. 10. Photograph of the dark side of the Moon obtained by *Lunik III*. Continuous and broken-line great circles are, respectively, the lunar equator and the boundary between the visible (left) and invisible (right) part of the Moon. Features known before: I. Mare Humboldtianum; II. Mare Crisium; III. Mare Marginis; IV. Mare Undarum; V. Mare Smythii; VI. Mare Fecunditatis; VII. Mare Australe. New features: 1. Mare Moscoviae; 2. Sinus Astronautarum; 3. Continuation of Mare Australe; 4. Ziolkovsky (crater); 5. Lomonosov (crater); 6. Joliot-Curie (crater); 7. Soviet mountain ridge; 8. Mare Desiderii.

tain that there is no water on the Moon and that its topography is much drier than the driest desert on the Earth.

Neither does the Moon possess any atmosphere, which can be

proved by observing the way stars disappear when the Moon in its motion across the sky obscures them by its advancing edge. If there were even a thin layer of air covering the Moon's surface, the stars would twinkle just before disappearing, and their apparent position would be slightly changed by refraction in the lunar atmosphere. The observations show, however, that stars disappear suddenly, as if cut off by a razor blade. Also the sharpness of shadows cast by lunar mountains indicates the absence of an atmosphere that would cause dawn and dusk, making the shadows considerably softer.

Illus. 9 shows a photograph of the entire face of the Moon turned toward us, and some characteristic local areas. Illus. 10 shows the opposite side of the Moon as observed from the Soviet rocket *Lunik III*. As was expected, both sides have a generally similar appearance. Large, darkish areas are the "seas," or *maria*, carrying such romantic names as *Mare Tranquillitatis* (Sea of Tranquillity), *Mare Serenitatis* (Sea of Serenity), *Mare Imbrium* (Sea of Showers), and a large desert plain on the right known as *Oceanus Procellarum* (Ocean of Storms). Mountain ranges are given names of various terrestrial mountains, so that we have lunar *Alps, Apennines, Carpathian* mountains and several others. The craters, most typical features of the lunar landscape, are mostly named after such great philosophers and scientists of the past as *Aristarchus, Archimedes, Plato, Copernicus, Tycho,* and *Kepler*.

The similar features on the opposite side of the Moon carry more Slavic names. There are the *Sea of Moscow,* the *Sea of Schmidt* (named for an influential living Russian astronomer), the *Soviet Mountains,* the *Crater of Lomonosov* (famous Russian scientist and poet of the eighteenth century), and the *Crater of Ziolkovsky* (a Russian schoolteacher who was a pioneer of rocket development and space travel). But in spite of the difference in names, the features of the lunar landscape are the same on both sides.

The principal problem of lunar geography, or more correctly *selenography,* is the origin of the craters which cover in large quantities all the surface of the Moon (Illus. 11). The largest

Ill. 11. Photograph of a part of the Moon's surface, showing the detailed structure of its craters.   *(Courtesy of the Yerkes Observatory)*

crater on the visible half of the Moon is *Clavius,* a wide circular plane 146 miles in diameter, surrounded by a steep wall 20,000 feet high. It is so large that, for an observer standing in the middle, the walls of the crater would be completely hidden below the horizon. The smallest craters visible to us with telescopes are not much larger than the Pentagon Building, and there are doubtless many still smaller ones.

What is the origin of lunar craters, and why are there so many of them? Until a few decades ago it was generally believed that the craters on the Moon were due to volcanic activity, as is the case for terrestrial craters such as Vesuvius or Fujiyama. But further studies have shown that this is not the case. Indeed, whereas the volcanic craters on the Earth usually have the shape of a sharply rising cone with a comparatively small depression on the top, a lunar crater looks more like a football stadium with a wide flat arena and a ring of stands around it. A formation of that kind could hardly be interpreted as the result of eruption of molten material from under the surface. On the other hand, there is a remarkable similarity between the lunar craters and the crater in Arizona which was proved to be due to the impact of a huge meteorite. When a massive object traveling at a velocity of about 10 miles per second strikes the ground, a tremendous amount of heat is developed at the point of impact. The meteorite itself and the ground in which it is buried melt and partially evaporate, throwing the material up and out in a large circle. The meteorite which produced Arizona's crater must have weighed about 200,000 tons and had a diameter of about 100 feet.

Craters of a size comparable to that in Arizona occur on the Moon in large numbers and are almost at the limit of visibility of a good telescope. The bigger craters must have been made by much larger meteorites. The crater Archimedes, which is 40 miles in diameter, was probably produced by a meteorite weighing about 25 billion tons, and the largest lunar crater, Clavius (146 miles in diameter), must have been the result of collision with a piece of cosmic matter weighing at least 200 billion tons. In the latter case, the meteorite must have been about four miles in diameter, comparable to a fairly large mountain on the Earth.

Why is the surface of the Moon covered with so many craters, including some of gigantic size, while on Earth there are only a few comparatively small craters, such as the rather mediocre one in Arizona? It certainly is unlikely that cosmic projectiles hit the Moon, which is so close to us, much more often than they hit the Earth. The correct explanation lies in the fact that since the Moon has no atmosphere its surface features are not subject to erosion by air and water as is the case with the Earth. A crater formed on the Moon a few thousand, million, or hundred million years ago looks today exactly as it looked when it first originated. On the other hand, meteor craters formed on the surface of the Earth are subject to continuous erosion and are gradually erased by rains washing away their material. The Arizona crater is only about eight thousand years old, and it is already eroded to quite a considerable extent; in another ten or twenty thousand years it may hardly be noticeable. An aerial survey of many parts of the Earth has proved the existence of a number of older meteor craters which are eroded to such an extent that no tourists would come to look at them.

Ill. 12. Tektites from the collection of Dr. Hans Suess at the University of California at La Jolla.

We cannot close the chapter on the Moon without mentioning what could be called "lunar tears." In several regions of the Earth (e.g., one on the Balkan Peninsula, another in Central Australia) geologists pick up very peculiar small objects known technically as *tektites*, which are found in various sedimentary layers of the past eras. Tektites, which were first discovered in 1899 by the Austrian geologist Eduard Suess, are composed of glassy material and sometimes look not unlike pieces of a broken beer bottle — a fact which induced Dr. Hans Suess (the son of Eduard), who studies these tektites at the University of Californit, to formulate a jocular hypothesis that the beer industry must have flourished on the Earth during early geological eras. Many tektites are shaped like mushrooms, with a regular hemispherical head and a stemlike structure below. From their shapes (Illus. 12) it is difficult to escape the impression that these bodies were heated to a partially molten state in a flight at high speed through the terrestrial atmosphere. The study of flowlines on tektites picked up in Australia suggests strongly their extraterrestrial origin, indicating that they entered the Earth's atmosphere at a speed of at least 4 miles per second. One cannot class them, however, with ordinary meteorites, which are formed either of a nickel-iron alloy or of stony material.

Our glass factories produce their goods by melting sand that is nearly pure silica, together with small quantities of other compounds. Could it be that tektites have a similar origin, being pieces of natural glass formed somewhere beyond the Earth under an exceptional thermal condition? One semi-fantastic but perhaps true hypothesis, proposed by Hans Suess, suggests that tektites came to the Earth from the Moon. Whenever a giant meteorite hit the Moon's surface, a spray of molten silicate compounds would be thrown into space. Since the Moon has no atmosphere, the spray would encounter no air resistance, and the molten drops thrown upward could escape the Moon's gravity and fly all the way to the Earth's surface. True or not, this possibility is very intriguing. One can speculate, for example, that the mysterious "rays" which spread in all directions from lunar craters are formed from similar glassy material that was projected in a more horizontal direction and fell on the Moon's surface. Thus it will be extremely interesting to pick up the material forming the "rays" and see if it is identical with tektites found on the Earth.

3

The Family of Planets

COMPARATIVE PLANETOLOGY

BEFORE GETTING DOWN to the main subject of this book, our own planet, let us make a brief survey of the other members of the solar system and compare their physical properties with those of the Earth. This "comparative planetology," as it may be called, will help us to understand the characteristics of our own planet, much in the same way as comparative anatomy gives biologists a better understanding of the human organism by comparing it with those of mosquitoes and elephants.

We find that some of the planets, such as Mercury, are so small, compared with the Earth, that the attraction of gravity at their surfaces is too slight to hold down their atmospheres, which escaped completely into interplanetary space soon after their formation.

FUGITIVE MOLECULES

To understand how planets lose their atmospheres, we must remember that the gaseous state of matter differs from the liquid and solid states in that gas molecules are free, incessantly darting back and forth in irregular zigzag paths and colliding with one another, while in liquids and solids the separate molecules are bound together by strong cohesive forces. Thus, if a gas is not surrounded on all sides by impenetrable walls, its molecules will rush off in all directions, and the gas will expand without limit into surrounding space.

In the case of our own atmosphere, which has no glass cover above it, of course, such unlimited expansion is hindered by the gravitational attraction of the Earth. The molecules of air that are moving upward against the force of gravity must soon lose their vertical velocity, much in the same way as an ordinary bullet does when shot into the sky. It is clear, however, that if we used some kind of "supergun" to give the bullet an initial velocity high enough to overcome the Earth's attraction, the bullet would escape into interplanetary space, never falling back to earth. From the known value of gravity at the surface of the Earth we can easily calculate that the "escape velocity" would have to be 7 miles per second, which can be achieved today by means of multistage rockets. The escape velocity for a given planet is independent of the projectile's mass; it is the same for a big-gun shell weighing a ton or more and for the minutest molecules of the air. The reason for this is that both the kinetic energy of the projectile and the gravitational forces acting upon it are proportional to its mass.

Thus, to determine whether the molecules of the atmosphere can escape from the Earth, we must know the velocities with which they move. Physics teaches us that molecular velocities increase with the temperature of the gas and are smaller for the molecules of the heavier elements. At the temperature at which water freezes, for example, the molecular velocities for hydrogen, helium, water vapor, nitrogen, oxygen, and carbon dioxide are 1.12, 0.81, 0.37, 0.31, 0.28, 0.25 miles per second, respectively; at 100° C. (212° F.) these velocities are increased by 17 per cent, and at 500° C. (932° F.) they are increased by 68 per cent. Comparing these figures with the 7 miles per second required for escape from the Earth, the reader would be inclined to believe that none of these gases could ever take flight from our atmosphere.

This conclusion is not quite correct, however, because the molecular velocities given above are merely *average values,* that is to say, most of the molecules are moving at these speeds, while there always is a small proportion of slower and faster molecules. The relative number of these exceptionally fast or exceptionally slow molecules is given by the distribution law formulated by James Clerk Maxwell. Using the Maxwell distribution law, we can calculate that the proportion of molecules possessing the velocity required to escape from the Earth is represented by a ridiculously small decimal fraction, with two hundred zeroes after the decimal point! But as there are always some molecules that can escape, they will do so, and their places will be taken by other molecules that formerly were moving more slowly. The percentage of such "fugitives" is considerably greater in the case of hydrogen molecules, which have a higher average velocity, while it is much lower for carbon dioxide molecules, whose average velocity is lower.

Thus we see that planetary atmospheres are gradually being "filtered" by this escape process, with large quantities of the heavier gases remaining long after the lighter gases are almost completely gone. As for "lost atmospheres," it is not a question of whether a given planet can lose its atmosphere (any planet can if given sufficient time!) but *whether the planet involved could have actually lost its atmosphere during the period of its existence.*

THE ATMOSPHERES OF PLANETS AND SATELLITES

Calculations have shown that the Earth is likely to have lost most of its atmospheric hydrogen and helium during the five billion years that have elapsed since its birth, whereas the heavier molecules of nitrogen, oxygen, water vapor, and carbon dioxide should have remained in large quantities. This explains why hydrogen is practically absent from our atmosphere, remaining on the Earth only in a combined form in water and certain other chemical compounds. It also explains why the inert gas helium, which forms practically no chemical compounds, is so rare on our planet, although astronomical evidence indicates it

Ill. 13. A phase of Venus. The brilliancy of this planet is due to the high
reflecting power of the thick clouds covering its daylight atmosphere.
(Courtesy of the Yerkes Observatory)

is abundant on the Sun and other stars and in interstellar clouds.

Following the dictates of chivalry, we shall now take up Venus,
which is the next smaller planet after the Earth and has an escape velocity of 6.7 miles per second, only slightly lower than
that of the Earth. Accordingly, we must expect Venus to have an
atmosphere only slightly more rarefied than our own, with large
quantities of water. As Venus is nearer the Sun than we are and
thus receives a correspondingly larger amount of solar radiation,
much of this water must be present in the form of clouds that
hide the beautiful face of the Goddess of Love and forever obscure it from our eyes. This white veil of clouds, illuminated by
the rays of the Sun, gives Venus an extremely high surface brightness and makes it the most brilliant of the planets (Illus. 13).

As for Mars (Illus. 14), which is the next smaller planet, possessing an escape velocity of only 3.1 miles per second, we must
expect to find an atmosphere much more rarefied than ours, an
expectation that agrees with the results of direct observation.
Illus. 14 shows two photographs of Mars, in which one half

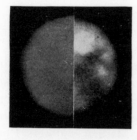 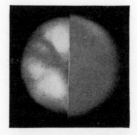

Ill. 14a. Two views of Mars, in which one half of the planet was photographed by ultraviolet light and the other by infrared light. Since infrared rays are easily reflected from the atmosphere, the larger size of the infrared image shows the extent of the Martian atmosphere.

(Courtesy of the Lick Observatory)

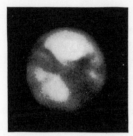 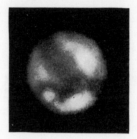

Ill. 14b. Two views of Mars, photographed on successive nights. Occasionally clouds may be observed as small white specks on the planet's surface, but by the following night they have completely disappeared.

of the planet was photographed by ultraviolet light and the other by infrared. As ultraviolet rays are greatly scattered by the atmosphere, details of the planet's surface do not show at all in that half, the image actually representing a photograph of the Martian atmosphere itself. Comparing this half of the image with the other half, taken by infrared light and unaffected by the atmosphere, we are able to observe the extent of that atmosphere. Another proof of the existence of an atmosphere on Mars is the fact that clouds can sometimes be observed as small white specks on the surface of the planet. These clouds, however, are considerably rarer than those over the Earth, from which we must conclude that water is rather scarce on the face of the bellicose planet. Although there are definite indications of the presence of water in liquid form on the surface of Mars, there are no big oceans comparable to ours, and the water is probably distributed in the form of extensive marshlands and shallow lakes.

Observing the surface of Mars, the Italian astronomer Giovanni Schiaparelli noticed something that looked like long, straight lines crossing the surface of the planet. Continuing his work, the American astronomer Percival Lowell became persuaded that these lines represent canals built by Martian engineers. However, more recent observations, which will be discussed later in this chapter, have led to the conclusion that Martian canals are just an optical illusion.

Now we come to the smallest of the original planets, Mercury, whose mass is twenty-five times smaller than the Earth's and whose escape velocity is only 2.1 miles per second. Being such a small planet, Mercury must have lost its atmosphere together with its water supply as soon as the gases were liberated from its cooling body.

The same situation prevails in even greater degree on the Moon (with an escape velocity of only 1.5 miles per second), as well as on all other satellites and all the asteroids. It is amusing to note that the force of gravity on the asteroid Eros is so small that a stone thrown upward by a good catapult would fly away and never return!

When we turn to the larger planets, Jupiter, Saturn, Uranus, and Neptune, with escape velocities of 38, 23, 13, 13.6 miles per second, respectively, we find an altogether different situation. The atmospheres of these giants among the planets not only retain oxygen, nitrogen, water vapor, and carbon dioxide, but also most of the hydrogen and helium that was present originally.

Since there is far more hydrogen than oxygen on the Sun, and consequently on these large planets as well, *all the oxygen would be present in a combined form in water, with none left in the atmosphere, which would consist chiefly of nitrogen, hydrogen, and helium.* We should also expect that, since hydrogen is present in such abundance, it will unite with carbon and nitrogen, forming the poisonous marsh gas, methane, and volatile compounds of ammonia, which will saturate this deadly atmos-

Ill. 15. Photograph of Jupiter, showing horizontal strata of atmospheric origin. The surface of the planet itself has never been seen.
(Courtesy of the Mount Wilson Observatory)

Ill. 16. Photograph of Saturn, showing atmospheric strata like those on Jupiter. The rings are formed by a great number of small particles revolving around the planet. *(Courtesy of the Mount Wilson Observatory)*

phere. Analysis of the sunlight reflected from these large planets does in fact show strong absorption lines due to these gases. On the other hand, spectroscopic analysis gives no indication of the presence of water vapor, which ought to be present in the atmosphere of these planets. This deficiency, however, is easily explained by the fact that their surface temperatures are so low (owing to their great distance from the Sun) that all water is precipitated in the form of snow and ice.

Illus. 15 and 16 are photographs of Jupiter and Saturn. The markings on the disks are of atmospheric origin, the solid crust of the planets being completely hidden by thick, opaque gaseous envelopes.

CONDITIONS FOR LIFE ON THE PLANETS

When we discuss the possibility of life on other planets, we come to a delicate point, for we do not actually know what life is or what forms of life different from those on the Earth are possible. Life in any form is doubtless totally impossible at the temperature of molten rock (above 1800° F.), or at absolute zero (−459.6°F.), at which all materials become quite rigid, but these are extremely wide limits. If we restrict ourselves to the ordinary forms of life found on the Earth, we can narrow these limits roughly to the temperature range in which water, the most essential constituent of organic structure, remains liquid. Some bacteria, of course, can stand boiling water with impunity for a time, while polar bears and Eskimos live in regions of perpetual frost. But in the first instance the death of the bacteria is only a question of time, and in the second we are dealing with highly developed organisms that keep themselves warm with furs and by a natural oxidation process within their bodies. From what we know of the evolution of life in the most elementary forms it can be concluded almost without doubt that life could not have originated or developed on the Earth if the oceans had forever boiled or had been frozen solid.

We can, of course, conceive of entirely different types of living cells, in which silicon might take the place of carbon, thus permitting these cells to endure considerably higher temperatures. Likewise, we can imagine organisms that contain alcohol instead of water, and therefore would not be frozen stiff at glacial temperatures. Yet, if such forms of life are possible, it is hard to understand why no such "alcoholic" animals and plants are found in our own polar regions, and why the boiling waters of geysers are absolutely devoid of "silicon life." Hence it seems quite probable that the conditions under which life is possible anywhere in the universe do not in general differ greatly from those under which life is possible on our Earth. Accepting this tentative assumption, let us now investigate the conditions for life on the various planets of the solar system.

Beginning our survey with the large outer planets, we must admit that there is hardly a chance for life to exist on their giant bodies. These planets are far too cold, as we have seen, and life is also out of the question there because their poisonous atmospheres contain neither oxygen nor carbon dioxide nor moisture.

Among the smaller "inner" planets, Mercury not only lacks air and water, but is so close to the Sun that the temperature on its daylight side rises high enough to melt lead! We may recall that only one of Mercury's hemispheres ever sees daylight, because the action of solar tides long ago slowed down the rotation of this planet so that it always turns the same side toward the great central body. Eternal night reigns on the opposite side, where the temperature is far below the freezing point of water — nor is there any water to freeze. *No, life cannot exist on Mercury!*

This leaves us with only two other planets, Venus and Mars, our inner and outer neighbors. Both possess atmospheres comparable to our own, and there are definite indications that both possess an adequate amount of water.

As far as surface temperatures are concerned, Venus must be, in general, somewhat warmer than the Earth, and Mars somewhat cooler. The permanent layer of thick clouds that obscures the surface of Venus makes an estimate of the temperature on the ground below rather difficult, but there is no reason to expect that the temperature and humidity on Venus are much worse than in the hot and humid tropical regions on Earth. Although Venus — like every modest woman — removes her veils only under cover of darkness, making it very difficult to obtain any definite information about its rotation by visual observations, some recent radar measurements indicate that Venus rotates at a very slow rate, possibly once in 225 days, which is the length of its period of revolution around the Sun. If this is so, there is no succession of day and night, and one side of Venus would be perpetually dark, always turned away from the Sun. This picture is not so encouraging on the whole, but we may infer that *some sort of life, at least, is possible on Venus.*

Whether life really does exist on Venus is quite a different matter, which at first glance seems wholly unanswerable because no one has ever seen its surface. Certain information concerning the presence of living cells on Venus, however, might be obtained from a spectroscopic analysis of its atmosphere. *The presence of any type of vegetation on a planet's surface would necessarily lead to a noticeable concentration of oxygen in its atmosphere,* inasmuch as it is the main physiological function of plants to decompose the carbon dioxide of the air, consuming the carbon in the process of growth and liberating oxygen. As we shall see later, all the oxygen in the Earth's atmosphere is probably due to this work of plants; *if some catastrophe caused the grassy fields and forests to vanish from the face of the Earth, atmospheric oxygen would soon disappear,* consumed in various oxidation processes. Spectroscopic analysis of the atmosphere of Venus fails to indicate free oxygen, though scientists would be able to detect as little as one-thousandth of the oxygen content of our own atmosphere. This leads us to conclude that *there is no extensive vegetation on the surface of Venus.* Without vegetation, animal life is scarcely possible, for, after all, animals cannot live simply by eating one another. Besides, there is no oxygen for them to breathe.

So it seems fairly certain that *life failed to develop on the surface of Venus for some reason or other,* despite relatively favorable conditions. This failure might be due to the thick layer of clouds on its daylight side, which might prevent the solar rays from penetrating to the surface in sufficient quantity to support the growth of plants.

On August 27, 1962, the interplanetary space observatory named *Mariner II* (the first one misfired) was launched by the United States toward the planet Venus. It was hurled into space by the Atlas-Agena combination rocket and flew to its rendezvous with Venus scheduled for December 14, 1962. *Mariner II* weighs 447 pounds, and in the folded state, while being lifted up by the rocket, was 5 feet in diameter and just under 10 feet in height. After entering interplanetary space, its solar panels and antennas were extended, making it 16.5 feet across and 12 feet high. The solar panels, resembling wings — which are of course unnecessary in the flight through vacuum — consisted of 9800 photocells occupying a total area of 27 square feet. They absorb radiation of the Sun and transform it into electric power ranging from 148 to 222 watts, depending on their position with respect to the Sun, which "never sets in space." The space probe contained a two-way radio set: 1) to receive instructions concerning the small changes of its course from its earthbound "pilots," who watch its progress through space; 2) to report its findings during the flight to the earthlings who designed and launched it.

Mariner II was equipped with a large variety of gadgets to provide information during its long flight and particularly during its closest approach to Venus on December 14, when it flew only about 20,900 miles (i.e., 2.5 diameters of the Earth) above Venus's surface. Microwave and infrared radiometers yielded valuable data concerning the properties of Venus's atmosphere, and a magnetometer measured the magnetic field of Venus as well as magnetic fields in space during the entire trip. There were also devices to measure the intensity of high-energy cosmic rays and low-energy particles emitted from the Sun. Finally, *Mariner II* carried a "sounding board" (5 inches by 10 inches) connected with a sensitive microphone which recorded the impacts of cosmic dust particles rushing widely through interplanetary, as well as through interstellar, space.

It was quite a rendezvous with the Goddess of Love! Preliminary analysis of the data received from *Mariner II* when it was passing close to Venus led to important conclusions concerning the magnetic field of that planet. A magnetometer which was aboard did not show any trace of a magnetic field similar to that which surrounds our Earth. This finding is in complete agreement with the theory of the origin of terrestrial magnetism, discussed in the following chapter, which ascribes the magnetic field of the Earth to convection in its iron core caused by the fast rotation of the Earth around its axis. As we have mentioned before, Venus is thought to rotate around its axis 225 times more slowly than the Earth does. Thus, no fast rotation, no convective currents in the core, no magnetic field.

If there is no magnetic field, one should not expect Venus to be surrounded by a region similar to the Van Allen belt (see p. 187), in which charged particles are captured by the Earth's magnetic field. And, indeed, the particle flux detector carried on board *Mariner II* found no radiation that would indicate the existence of such a belt. Poor old Goddess of Love! No compasses, no Van Allen belt, and presumably no beautiful polar lights in her northern region.

THE ARID FACE OF MARS

Our outer neighbor Mars is the only planet whose surface can be observed in some detail, and hence far more is known about it than about all the other planets together. At its closest approach to the Earth, Mars is only 34,797,000 miles away, and its atmosphere is clear and transparent, with only occasional small clouds. Spectroscopic analysis of its atmosphere shows only small traces of free oxygen and moisture.

Because of its comparatively low escape velocity the atmosphere of Mars is now considerably more rarefied than ours, with an atmospheric pressure only one-tenth of that of the Earth. An astronaut on Mars would be subjected to the same atmospheric conditions that an airplane pilot would encounter at extremely great altitudes. Since its formation Mars has apparently also lost nearly all of its water, and the climate of that planet is probably quite dry.

As seen through the telescope, Mars presents a rather smooth surface without noticeable mountain ranges like those on the Earth.* There are, however, permanent markings on the surface of Mars that suggest a definite type of landscape. About five-eighths of the surface is ruddy or orange-colored, giving the planet the generally reddish tint that led the ancients to associate it with the God of War. The coloring of these areas always remains unchanged, and it is fairly certain that they are rocky or sandy expanses devoid of vegetation. The other three-eighths of the planet's surface consists of bluish-grey or greenish regions which were originally thought to be large basins of water much like our oceans and seas. Because of this assumption these regions still bear such names as *Mare Sirenum* and *Sinus Margaritifer*. But these darker areas are not water surfaces, for if they were, they would be much more uniform in color and, what is much more important, they would reflect the rays of the Sun brilliantly under favorable conditions. The bluish and greenish tints suggest, on the other hand, the presence of vegetation, and this hypothesis receives strong support from observed seasonal changes in their coloring. In fact, the greenish coloring of these regions is most conspicuous during the spring period of the hemisphere in which they lie, steadily fading and turning yellowish brown as the winter period approaches. It is extremely difficult to conceive that anything but vegetation like that on our Earth would be able to produce all these effects, and spectroscopic studies of the American astronomer G. P. Kuiper indicate that *the darker regions could be plains covered with mosses or lichens, such as those covering terrestrial rocks.*

Although no apparent areas of free water can be discovered on the surface of Mars, there is ample evidence of snow and ice, which form two brilliantly white caps at the poles of the planet (Illus. 17). The seasonal changes of Mars are, of course, most

---

* Such mountains on the surface of Mars would be easily discernible by the long shadows they would cast during the planet's sunset.

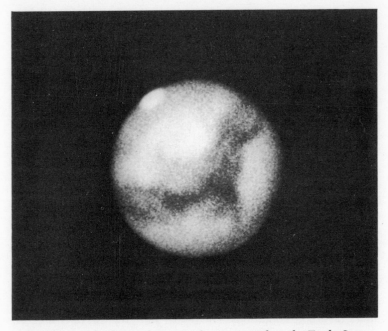

Ill. 17. Photograph of Mars during its closest approach to the Earth, September 28, 1909. The white spot at the top is the polar ice cap. The lighter parts of the surface represent deserts, while the darker ones are probably lowlands covered with lichens and moss. *(Courtesy of the Yerkes Observatory)*

noticeable at its polar caps. During the winter periods they extend almost halfway to the equator (in terrestrial terminology we should say that snow falls at the latitude of Boston), the rays of the Sun pushing them back to the poles again in the spring. The southern polar cap sometimes disappears completely during the hottest days of summer in the southern hemisphere. In Mars's northern hemisphere, which is the colder of the two (precisely the opposite of the state of affairs on the Earth*), the snow never

---

* Owing to the ellipticity of the Earth's orbit, the Earth is closer to the Sun during the northern winter and farther from it during the northern summer. This makes winters in the Northern Hemisphere milder and summers cooler, while the Southern Hemisphere has colder winters and warmer summers. The colder winter in the Southern Hemisphere results in the formation of an antarctic polar ice cap that is larger than the one at the North Pole.

disappears completely; it is merely reduced to a tiny white spot near the north pole. The disappearance of the polar caps on Mars is due not to its warmer climate (we know that it is colder than the Earth), but to the comparative rareness of water, which prevents the formation of a thick ice sheet. If snow formed only thin layers of ice at the Earth's poles, these layers would melt away under the Sun even more quickly than the Martian polar caps.

Study of the growth and melting of polar caps offers a useful method of estimating the comparative heights of different landscape features on Mars. When the snow line retreats toward the poles in the spring, some white spots remain behind for a time, evidently indicating higher regions. Moreover, it is in these regions that snow first begins to fall with the approach of winter.† Since the "first snow" always appears on the reddish parts of the planet, we must conclude not only that they represent comparatively elevated regions, but that vegetation is concentrated at the lower levels. The difference in height between the upper and lower regions of Mars, however, is not very great; it is certainly much less than it would be on the Earth if the waters of the oceans should diffuse into interplanetary space, leaving the ocean floors exposed to the air and covered with vegetation.

Temperatures on the surface of Mars, which seems to be the most comfortable place for life to exist beyond our Earth within the solar system, are also of some interest. Measurements made with the bolometer, a highly sensitive instrument that records the amount of heat radiated by objects at vast distances, indicate that the noon temperature is only 50° F. or possibly slightly higher along the equator. Just after sunrise or before sunset the temperature must be well below the freezing point of water even in the equatorial regions, while the nights must be very cold.*

---

† Nowhere on the surface of Mars can we observe permanent ice formations like the eternal snow of mountain regions on the Earth. This is an additional proof of the absence of high mountains on Mars.

* Occasionally small white specks are observed near the sunrise area of Mars; they disappear rapidly when the Sun rises higher over that area. There is no doubt that these white specks are quite similar to the hoarfrost formed on the surface of the Earth during cold nights.

The polar regions, of course, are much colder; at the ice caps the temperature is probably as low as $-94°$ F. Such a climate can hardly be called comfortable, but it is far from prohibitive for vegetable or even animal life.

Some sixty years ago a romantic announcement by Percival Lowell caused great excitement in the scientific world and among the general public. Lowell claimed to have discovered proof, not only of the existence of animal life, but also of a high degree of culture among the "inhabitants" of Mars.

His claim was based upon the so-called "Martian canals," a geometrical network of perfectly straight, narrow, sharply defined lines on the surface of the planet that had been first reported by Giovanni Schiaparelli in 1877 and since described by several other observers (Illus. 18). If such "canals" actually existed, their geometrically perfect regularity could be explained only as the result of the activity of intelligent beings. And Lowell developed a bold and ingenious theory according to which these canals were constructed by Martians who, facing a scarcity of water, built a giant irrigation system in their desperate struggle for life on the dying planet. According to Lowell, the surface canals represented regions of parks and gardens stretching along these artificial waterways, which cross the barren, red-tinted deserts. He imagined that at the beginning of spring in one of the hemispheres, when the snow of one polar cap began to melt, the resulting water was artificially pumped along these canals to supply the dry equatorial regions, and he even made an attempt to estimate the velocity of the water flow in the canals from the progressive changes in their color.

These speculations are extremely exciting, and they would also be of great value if the "canals" actually existed. Unfortunately, however, they do not, as has been proved by observation made with superior telescopes and by advanced photographic methods. It seems that the network of canals reported by so many observers is simply an optical illusion arising from the tendency of the human eye to connect details by narrow lines forming a geometrical pattern whenever it looks at something near the limit of visibility. There are innumerable dark spots on the surface of Mars,

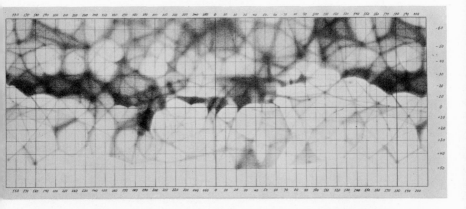

Ill. 18. A map of the Martian canals as drawn by R. J. Trumpler from visual observation in 1924. More recent observations prove the canals to be optical illusions. *(Courtesy of the Lick Observatory)*

but no straight lines or canals connecting them! And Kuiper's studies, carried on in 1956, indicate that Mars is uninhabitable except for a very primitive type of vegetation.

ODD MEMBERS OF THE SOLAR SYSTEM

Apart from the regular planets and their satellites, the solar system possesses several "oddities" which may have originated some time after its formation. We have already mentioned the ring of asteroids which move in the gap between Mars and Jupiter where, according to the Titus-Bode rule and Weizsäcker's theory, an extra planet should be found. Although most asteroids move in the region about halfway between Mars and Jupiter, some of them exceed these limits. On its closest approach to the Sun the asteroid Eros, for example, crosses the orbit of Mars and can be observed at a distance of only 13,800,000 miles from the Earth. On the other hand, Hidalgo, the most distant asteroid, reaches the point outside of the orbit of Jupiter. The largest asteroids, such as Ceres, Pallas, Juno, and Vesta, are several hundred miles in diameter, while the smallest visible ones are "mountains broken loose" no more than ten miles across. In spite of their comparatively large number, the combined mass of all the known asteroids is small compared with the Earth's, and, even allowing for smaller, as yet undiscovered, members of this family, one comes to the conclusion that the total mass of the swarm is not much larger than one per cent of the Earth's.

As we saw in Chapter I, the meteorites which fall on the surface of the Earth and are stored in our museums apparently belong to the same family as the asteroids, and their chemical analysis can tell us something about the origin of the asteroid ring. The studies in this direction indicate that material of meteorites must have crystallized under very high pressure, a conclusion which is also supported by the fact that small diamonds have been found in several iron meteorites. These findings strongly support the theory that meteorites and presumably asteroids are the fragments of a large planet which once moved in an orbit between Mars and Jupiter, and are not condensations of the original material of the solar envelope which for some reason never formed a planet.

Another oddity in the solar system is the planet Pluto, discovered in 1930 on the basis of theoretical calculations. Pluto moves beyond the orbit of Neptune along a rather unusual orbit. While all planetary orbits are very nearly circles, and are only very slightly tilted in respect to the plane of ecliptics, Pluto's orbit is strongly elongated and its tilt is about 18 degrees. It is interesting to notice that while at its largest distance from the Sun Pluto gets out into space much farther than Neptune, its closest approach to the Sun is somewhat smaller than the radius of Neptune's orbit, so that two orbits actually intersect. From the direct observation of Pluto's diameter, astronomers concluded that its mass is only 3 per cent of that of the Earth, which would make it the smallest member of the planetary family. All this leads to the conclusion that Pluto is probably not one of the original planets but a former satellite of Neptune which was kicked out into the solar orbit as the result of gravitational conflict with two other satellites of Neptune: Triton and Nereid. The orbits of these two remaining satellites bear the evidence of that battle which took place billions of years ago: Triton revolves around Neptune in the retrograde direction, while the orbit of Nereid is highly eccentric.

Beyond Pluto's orbit lies a wide region populated by comets which once in a while come close inside of the system of planets and develop brilliant tails under the action of the intensive solar radiation. The study of comets indicates that they are formed mostly from hydrogen compounds of carbon, nitrogen, and oxygen (methane, ammonia, and water), i.e., the substances which comprised the atmospheres of the planets during their formation and were later blown away by the radiation pressure of the sunlight. This completes our description of the main features of the solar system.

4

Hell below Our Feet

THE DEEPER THE HOTTER

THE CLOUDS OF BLACK SMOKE coming from the craters of active
volcanoes and the red-hot lava pouring down their slopes, the
hot springs and the spouting geysers led people of the ancient
world to believe that there was blazing fire not too far underfoot
for sinners after their death.

In the middle of the nineteenth century a famous German
geologist, Professor Otto Liedenbrock, found in an old volume
borrowed from a university librarian a piece of parchment with
a text in ancient Icelandic runic writing. Translating it into Latin,
he discovered a cryptogram which was deciphered to mean:

*Descend into the crater of Snaeffels Jokull that lies under
Scartaris' shadow, bold traveler, and you will reach the center
of the Earth as I have.*

— Arne Saknussemm

A quick check proved that Arne Saknussemm was a Scandinavian alchemist of the sixteenth century who was accused of
heresy and burned at the stake on a fire made of the books he
had written, and that Snaeffels Jokull was an inactive volcano
rising above one of Iceland's glaciers. Accompanied by his
nephew Axel and the hired guide named Hans from Reykjavik,
Professor Liedenbrock descended into the crater and, by follow-

ing a long inclined corridor through basalt rocks, reached a large underground sea which stretched beyond the limits of sight. They could extinguish their torches here, since sufficient illumination was provided by a diffuse glowing light, presumably resulting from some kind of chemiluminescence of rocks. Hans built a raft, and they set sail in a southeastern direction. After many days of perilous travel, during which their raft was almost overturned when an ichthyosaurus and a plesiosaursus (see Chapter 10) started a titanic battle near it, they finally came to the opening of a tunnel which, according to the markings left by Arne Saknussemm, led to the center of the Earth. But, since the famous alchemist had visited here three centuries ago, the passage had been closed by rockfall, and they had to use a powerful explosive charge to blow their way through. The blast opened a large crack, and the waters of the underground sea rushed through it toward the center of the Earth, carrying along the raft and the travelers. But somewhere midway the downcoming stream of water encountered an upgoing stream of red-hot molten lava, and they found themselves floating up toward the Earth's surface while the wooden logs of their raft were rapidly charred and threatened to burst into flames. Fortunately, before anything catastrophic had happened, they were thrown clear out of the crater of the volcano Stromboli in Italy.

As the reader may already have suspected, this account is not taken from the pages of some geological magazine of that time, but from a book called *Journey to the Center of the Earth*, written by the famous French fiction writer Jules Verne, and published in 1864. Today we have much better methods for studying the interior of the Earth: instead of descending into volcanic craters we can use the information obtained by boring deep holes in the Earth's crust.

Even with the comparatively small range of attainable depths, investigations reveal one extremely important fact: *the temperature of the rocks steadily increases as we dig deeper and deeper beneath the surface*. In deep mines the temperature always rises rather high, and in the world's deepest gold mine, the Robinson Deep (South Africa), for example, the walls are so hot that a half-million-dollar air-conditioning plant had to be installed to prevent the miners from being roasted alive. The most comprehensive data about the temperature distribution under the surface of the Earth are obtained from deep well-borings carried on in several thousand different localities all over the surface of the globe. Measurements in such wells show that *temperature increase with depth is quite a general phenomenon* and is practically independent of the geographic site of the observation station. Close to the surface there are always some deviations from uniformity because of the prevailing climatic conditions, and rocks situated only a few hundred feet under the polar tundras are naturally somewhat colder than those under the Sahara Desert. Measurements made in wells bored through the ocean floor also indicate that the temperature of rocks under the water surface is lower than those at the same depth under the continents. All these differences, however, are limited to a comparatively thin outer layer of the crust, and at greater depths the surfaces of equal temperatures run closely parallel to the surface

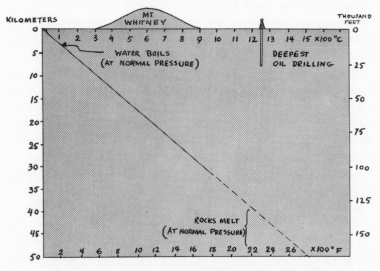

Ill. 19. Increase of temperature of the Earth with increase in depth below its surface.

Ill. 20. "Old Faithful," a geyser in Yellowstone National Park (photographed at night). Periodic eruptions of hot water and steam are due to the fact that the water from the surface of the Earth leaks down through cracks in the crust and, reaching a depth of only one and a half miles, is heated to the boiling point by contact with the hot rocks of the interior.

(Courtesy of the U.S. Geologic Survey)

of the globe. Illus. 19, which gives the observed temperature changes in the accessible outer layer of the crust, shows that *the increase of temperature is remarkably steady there, amounting to an average of about 16° F. per thousand feet.*

Since the average temperature of the Earth's surface is about 68° F., *the temperature of rocks rises to the boiling point of water at a depth of only one and a half miles.* If water from the surface of the Earth, leaking through occasional cracks in the crust, reaches this depth, it begins to boil and is ejected by vapor pressure in the form of the magnificent hot geysers so familiar to visitors to Yellowstone National Park (Illus. 20).

If the rise of temperature continues at the same rate through the first few dozen miles beyond the explored region, *the temperature of molten rocks (i.e., between 2200° and 3300° F.) must be reached at a depth of about 30 miles below the surface.* There seems to be no doubt that the molten lava that is ejected by the numerous volcanoes on the surface of the Earth originates at approximately the same depth. In fact, measurements of lava temperature inside the volcanic craters always yield the value of about 2200° F., corresponding to a depth of about 30 miles. Volcanic eruptions, which long before the foundation of scientific geophysics led the ancients to the hypothesis that "Hell" is situated somewhere under their feet, give us the best proof of the thinness of the solid crust upon which we base all our life.

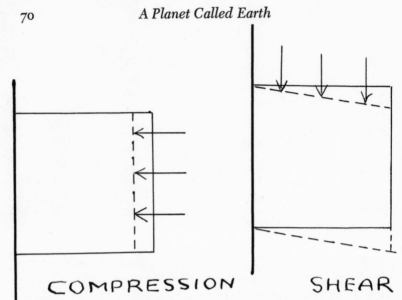

COMPRESSION   SHEAR

Ill. 21. Effects of compression and shear on a cube fastened to the wall.

THE EARTH QUAKES

As a physician using a stethoscope can study the interior condition of his patient without opening him up, a modern geophysicist can get information concerning the deep interior of the Earth by studying the elastic waves propagating through its body. The natural source of such elastic waves is provided by the deformations of the Earth's crust. Many a time the crustal rocks in one or another region of deformation are not able to withstand the tension, and crack as does a nutshell in a nutcracker. These local underground catastrophes result in the trembling of the Earth's crust in their neighborhood, and, in especially severe cases, all over the surface of the globe. The science of *seismology*, which studies these phenomena, commonly known as earthquakes, tells us much about the physical properties of the interior of the Earth through which the seismic waves are propagating. On a smaller scale, similar studies can be carried out by exploding charges ranging from a few pounds of TNT to an H-bomb, and studying the propagation of elastic deformations caused by them through the body of the Earth.

Solid materials, be they rocks, metals, or rubber, resist external forces tending to change their volume or their shape. If a cube made of elastic material is fastened to a solid wall (Illus. 21) and we apply pressure in a direction perpendicular to the wall, the cube will be compressed but will return to the original volume when the pressure is removed. Different materials have various degrees of compressibility, depending on their internal structures.

There is another way of deforming a solid body, which changes its shape rather than its volume. Indeed, if instead of pressing against the side of the cube we apply a downward force on its upper surface, the shape of the cube will change but its volume will remain the same. Such a deformation is known as a *shear* and is rather different from the compression just described. The resistance to a shearing force in different materials also depends on their internal structures, but differently from the way resistance to compression does. Liquids, for example, show about the same resistance to compression as solids do, while, on the other hand, they do not resist at all any change of their shape.

Let us consider now a long solid rod which is hit by a hammer at one of its ends (Illus. 22). If the impact is delivered along the rod's axis, the material at that end will be compressed, and this compression will propagate with a certain velocity all along its length. If, on the other hand, a blow is delivered perpendicular to the rod's axis, it results in a shear, i.e., a change of shape without change of volume. This deformation will also propagate along the axis with a certain velocity, depending on how strongly the material of the rod resists the shearing force. The velocity of compression or pressure waves (*P*-waves) is, generally speaking, different from the velocity of shear waves (*S*-waves), and in most materials *P*-waves propagate about twice as fast as *S*-waves.

If, in the example cited, one hits the rod with a hammer at,

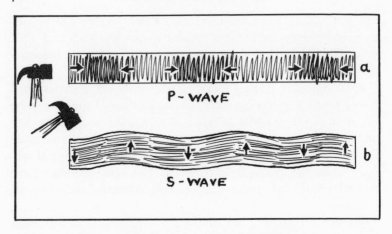

Ill. 22. Pressure and shear waves in a solid rod. In the top bar the dark
areas are regions of compression; the light areas are regions of expansion.
All displacements are drawn to an exaggerated scale.

let us say, a 45-degree angle in respect to its axis, both waves
will be produced, and the compression wave will run well ahead
of the shear wave. This is exactly what is to be expected and is
actually observed when an earthquake wave, propagating
through the body of the Earth from the center of disturbance,
comes to the surface some distance away from its source (epicenter). To measure Earth movements during a quake, seismolo-
gists use sensitive instruments known as *seismographs*. These
instruments are based essentially on the law of inertia, according
to which any material body at rest tends to preserve its state of
rest.

There are many different systems of seismographs, one of
which, known as the horizontal pendulum, is shown schematically in Illus. 23. It consists essentially of a heavy weight *A*,
which can move with very little friction around the vertical pole
B. If the ground on which this apparatus is resting is jerked by
the earthquake wave in the direction perpendicular to the plane
of the drawing, weight *A* remains immovable because of its
large inertia, and the displacement of the stand relative to the

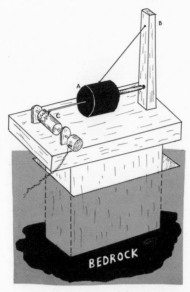

Ill. 23. The principle of the seismograph, known as the horizontal pendulum.

weight is registered on the rotating cylinder *C*. Two such instruments installed at right angles to each other give complete information concerning the horizontal displacement caused by the quake. In order to measure vertical displacement, one uses a weight suspended on a spring. When the Earth's surface jerks up and down, the weight remains at rest, and the relative motion of the weight and the stand can also be registered on a rotating cylinder. Combining all these data, one obtains detailed information about the direction and the intensity of surface displacement caused by the quake.

The possibility of distinguishing between *P*- and *S*-waves is based on the fact that the ground motion caused by the *P*-waves is in the same direction as that in which they propagate, while the motion caused by *S*-waves is at a right angle to their direction of propagation. And, indeed, one observes two successive shocks with a short quiet period between them, the first being due to the *P*-wave and the second to the *S*-wave.

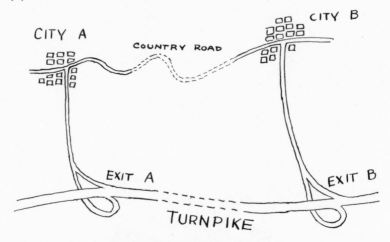

Ill. 24a. Two different routes between distant cities. The turnpike trip may
be faster, though longer than the route by country road.

THE MOHOROVIČIĆ DISCONTINUITY

On October 8, 1909, a strong earthquake originating in Kulpa
Valley in Croatia shook this little country and sent out waves
that were recorded in many seismographic stations throughout
Europe. The records showed two sets of *P*- and *S*-waves, which
were ascribed to a double tremor. The matter seemed to be quite
trivial. But it didn't look trivial at all to a Croatian-born seismologist, Andrija Mohorovičić, who tried to get an over-all picture of
what had happened as the result of a quake in his own, his
native land. Comparing the data recorded by the stations located
at different distances from the point of origin, he found that
there was something wrong about the arrival times of the two
P-waves which were followed in due course by the respective
S-waves. At distances less than 100 miles from the epicenter the
P- and *S*-wave group which arrived first was very violent, and
was followed by a much weaker second *P*- and *S*-wave group. At
larger distances, however, the situation was reversed and a weak

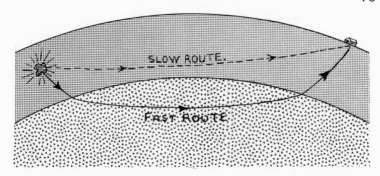

Ill. 24b. Mohorovičić discontinuity. Quake waves moving deeper underground arrived first at points located at great distances.

P- and S-wave group was followed, after a considerable delay, by a stronger one. This delay increased regularly with the distance of the recording stations from the epicenter.

The only possible way to explain these facts was to assume that there was only one tremor in Croatia, but that the seismic waves which were propagating from the center of disturbance could take two different routes: a slower one, and a faster one. Imagine a turnpike, and a slower, older road several miles away from it passing through the cities *A, B, C,* etc. (See Illus. 24a) One can reach all these cities by the turnpike by taking the proper exit. A man living in *A* and going to visit a friend in *B* has two choices: 1) to drive all the way by the old road *AB;* 2) to drive to the nearest turnpike entrance, follow the turnpike for a while, and then turn off at the next exit. If the distance from *A* to *B* is small, he will get there faster by not taking the turnpike. But if the distance is long, it is certainly more reasonable to lose some time getting to the turnpike, and then overcompensate that loss by driving along it very fast.

Following this analogy, Mohorovičić assumed that, at a certain depth under the Earth's surface, there exist rocks through which seismic waves can propagate much faster than they can through the upper crustal layers. Thus, the earthquake waves which, instead of going straight to a distant station, go through the deeper layer of the Earth's body will get there first (Illus. 24b).

He calculated that in the continent of Europe this "earthquake turnpike" is located about 35 miles below the surface, and that the earthquake waves penetrating that deep run about twice as fast as those propagating closer to the surface. Since the velocity of the earthquake waves is generally larger in heavier materials, Mohorovičić assumed that below that depth the material of the globe must be much denser than the granite and basalt rocks forming the outer crust. It may be, for example, that these underlying rocks contain much more iron than the rocks forming the outer crust.

Further studies have proved that this boundary between the lighter outer crust and the heavier inner region, generally known as the *mantle*, continues all around the Earth. However, whereas in the continental areas the Mohorovičić discontinuity is located some 20 miles below sea level, the crust is much thinner in the case of ocean basins, and the crust-mantle boundary is located only about 3 miles below the bottom of the ocean.

Due to the difficulty encountered by English-speaking people in pronouncing complicated foreign names, the Mohorovičić discontinuity is known in this country just as *Moho,* and the term *Mohole* is used for Moho-hole, a project for the drilling of a hole in the Earth's crust deep enough to reach the mantle lying below it. Since drilling a well 20 miles deep below the surface of a continent to reach Moho is a clearly impossible undertaking, the only hope of reaching it and of finding out the nature of the material of which the mantle of the Earth is composed is to drill through the thin crust at the bottom of the ocean. Of course, to start drilling the ocean bottom one has to sink the drills from aboard a surface vessel all the way through the water, which may be several miles deep, but then it is only a matter of two or three miles of actual drilling. Illus. 25 shows the profile of the Earth's crust, in the vicinity of Puerto Rico, obtained by the Lamont Geological Observatory on the basis of seismic and gravitational measurements. The arrow indicates the location from which the drilling in this vicinity would be most successful.

The idea of deep-ocean drilling originated one hot summer day of 1952 in the Office of Naval Research in Washington, D.C.,

PUERTO RICO

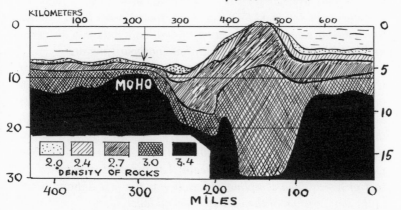

Ill. 25. Section of the Earth's crust in the vicinity of Puerto Rico, according to the Lamont Geological Observatory.

and later became a nation-wide project under the guidance of the National Academy of Sciences and the National Research Council, with the technical help of various oil companies which had had a lot of experience with ocean-bottom drilling, at least in shallow waters. The report entitled "Experimental Drilling in Deep Water at La Jolla and Guadalupe Sites," published in 1961 by the National Academy of Sciences and the National Research Council, summarizes in the following words the results of the first attempt at drilling:

In April 1961 the world's first oceanic drilling experiments were successfully completed. Two years of planning and preparation had been required in which theoretical and model studies of the drilling ship and its equipment gradually gave way to engineering design, purchase of equipment, shipyard installation and deep water operations.

The drilling barge CUSS I was modified in a San Diego, California shipyard and the first tests were conducted in March at a

77

site off La Jolla. There, in water 3111 feet deep, five holes were drilled into the sea floor to a maximum depth of 1035 feet. Shortly thereafter the ship was towed to a site 40 miles east of Guadalupe Island, Mexico for the first drilling in a true oceanic environment. In water 11,672 feet deep, the ship held itself above the hole by sensing the position of taut-wire buoys with sonar and radar, and maneuvering with four outboard motors.

The drill pipe was lowered and the bit was drilled in wherever it touched down on the soft bottom. No means was provided for hole reentry or for return circulation of drilling fluid. More or less continuous cores were retrieved by wire-line methods through the drill pipe. Five holes were drilled, each with a specific objective, to a maximum depth of 601 feet. The uppermost 557 feet was largely Miocene ooze; beneath that the drill penetrated 44 feet of basalt. The sampling of basalt was the first definite proof of the composition of the oceanic "second layer."

Ten geophysical logs were run; the temperature of the sediments at depth was measured, and the deep ocean current structure was recorded in a new way. A wire-line-coring diamond-bitted turbo-drill experimentally cored the basalt.

The ship left the drilling site on April 12 and thence was demobilized and restored to its previous condition.

It was concluded that virtually any drilling operation which can be performed in a hole on land can be done in the deep ocean as long as the bit need not be replaced.

THE DEEP INTERIOR

The thickness of the crust as compared with the Earth's radius is just about the same as the thickness of the skin of an apple as compared with its radius, and the success of the Mohole project in determining the composition of the mantle will be equivalent to scratching a tiny bit of apple skin and finding that, inside, the apple is actually white rather than red. Quite a success — but still just a beginning! However, although we cannot possibly drill a hole all the way to the center of the Earth, or even more than

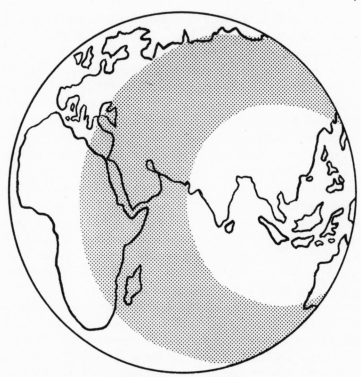

Ill. 26. Earthquake shadow zone for a disturbance radiating from Peru
(the sharpness of the zone limits is exaggerated).

skin deep, we get very valuable information about the Earth's
interior by the study of seismic waves, by means of which, as we
have seen, the Mohorovičić discontinuity was discovered. In the
case of very strong disturbances, which can be recorded all over
the Earth's surface, the waves are propagated all across the body
of the Earth, and the study of their arrival at different points on
the globe permits us to penetrate with our mind's eye virtually to
the very center of the planet. The most striking fact revealed by
observations of such long-distance quakes is the existence of the
so-called *shadow zone,* that is, a broad belt on the surface of the
globe in which the disturbance passes practically unnoticed
(Illus. 26). If, for example, the epicenter of the earthquake is

somewhere in Peru, a strong disturbance will be noticed all over the Western Hemisphere and also in the part of the Eastern Hemisphere situated around the point which is exactly opposite to the quake's origin, i.e., in India, Indochina, and the East Indies. However, the seismographs located in a belt passing through Siberia, Arabia, West Africa, the Indian Ocean, southeastern Australia, and the western Pacific will behave as if nothing had happened. Furthermore, whereas the quake waves emerging to the Earth's surface between the epicenter and the outer rim of the shadow zone contain both P and S components, only P-waves appear in the circular region within the shadow zone.

These astonishing facts can be explained only by the assumption that our globe contains in its interior a liquid core made of some very heavy material which extends out from the center to about 60 per cent of the Earth's radius. Since, as we have discussed, S-waves cannot propagate through a liquid material, such a core will completely stop all S-waves from getting into the hemisphere opposite to that in which the quake originated. On the other hand, a heavy liquid core which can carry P-waves will act as a lens, focusing them in the region directly opposite the point of their origin, and leaving a "dark" ring around it. Thus, the resulting picture of the distribution of earthquake disturbances will look exactly as it is depicted in Illus. 27.

Ill. 27. Distribution and speed of earthquake waves from the epicenter to various stations on the earth's surface.

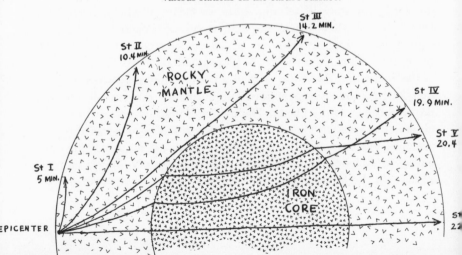

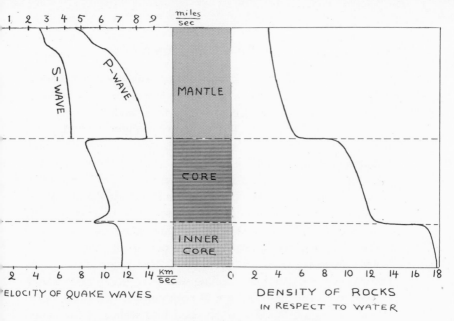

miles/sec

1 2 3 4 5 6 7 8 9

S-WAVE

P-WAVE

MANTLE

CORE

INNER CORE

2 4 6 8 10 12 14 km/sec

VELOCITY OF QUAKE WAVES

0 2 4 6 8 10 12 14 16 18

DENSITY OF ROCKS
IN RESPECT TO WATER

Ill. 28. Mechanical properties of the Earth's body.

In Illus. 28 we give the most recent results (collected by the well-known seismologist Beno Gutenberg) concerning the observed propagation velocities of seismic waves at different depths between the surface and the center of the Earth. We notice first that both *P*- and *S*-waves propagate down to the distance of about 1800 miles below the surface of the Earth. The fact that *S*-waves, which cannot propagate through liquid material, reach that depth, proves that the body of the Earth is solid down to about halfway from the surface to the center.

PLASTIC MANTLE

The fact that seismic shear waves can penetrate nearly half-way to the Earth's center seems at first glance to contradict an earlier statement that, at the rate at which the temperature in the Earth's crust increases with the depth, the rocks must reach their melting point at a depth of only about 30 miles below the surface. How, therefore, are they able to carry shear waves at far greater depths, where their temperatures must be much

81

higher? To answer this question we must remember that, besides being subjected to extremely high temperatures, the rocks at great depths are also subjected to extremely high pressure. And, from what we know about the properties of matter, we may suspect that the combination of very high pressure and very high temperatures may bring the material to a rather unusual physical state, in which it has the combined properties of solid and liquid bodies. It will react as an elastic solid in respect to comparatively strong outside forces lasting for comparatively short periods of time. But it will behave as a liquid when acted upon by much weaker forces which last for very long periods of time.

This property, known as plasticity, is also possessed by some familiar materials, such as a sealing wax. If we try to bend a stick of sealing wax while holding it at both ends, it will break up as if made of glass. But if it is attached to a wall in a horizontal position, thus being supported at only one end, we shall find that days or weeks later (depending on the room temperature) it has arched down under its own weight.

Apparently this property of plasticity is possessed by the hot and strongly compressed rocks forming the mantle of the Earth. They act as "beauty rest" mattresses for the huge continental masses resting on them, and, in the course of millennia, bend in or bulge out to accommodate the weight they support. In the next chapter we shall see, in fact, that this cushion activity of the mantle rocks plays an important role in the development of the surface features of our planet.

On the other hand the mantle material reacts too slowly in respect to the rapidly varying forces exerted by a propagating earthquake wave, and, in all practical respects, behaves as a perfect elastic solid. In Chapter 2, in the discussion of ocean tides, we stated that there are also "tides in rocks," and that the entire body of the Earth is being deformed by gravity forces exerted by the Moon and the Sun with a 12-hour period. From the observed magnitude of these deformations, the famous British physicist Lord Kelvin was able to calculate that the body of the Earth is as rigid as if it were made of steel. Thus, apparently even 12 hours is too short a time-period to reveal the plastic

Ill. 29. The Earth, with a segment of the solid outer crust and the plastic
mantle cut away, showing the central iron core.

properties of the rocks forming the mantle of the Earth. But,
given a considerably longer time, they will flow like honey, as
will be discussed in the next chapter.

THE IRON CORE

At the depth of about 1800 miles the properties of the material
forming our globe suddenly change. No shear wave can propagate beyond that limit, which means that the material here is a
fluid, and the sharp decrease in the velocity of pressure waves
indicates that this fluid is ten times denser than water. It is generally accepted (although some geophysicists still deny it) that

the core is made of a molten mixture of iron, nickel, and chromium (Illus. 29). There is no way of proving that statement directly, but plenty of circumstantial evidence exists. The density of the core is just about equal to the density that iron is expected to have when subjected to the high pressures existing at that depth. Iron, which according to astronomical evidence is rather abundant in the universe, is comparatively scanty in the Earth's crust, suggesting the possibility that, being very heavy, it mostly sank to the center of the Earth. Granite rocks at the surface of the Earth contain practically no iron; the basalt layer underneath contains a considerable amount of iron; and the material of the mantle is probably still richer in that element. Thus it would be no wonder if the core itself was nothing but iron. About ten per cent of the meteorites, which may represent fragments of a planet that once upon a time traveled in an orbit between those of Mars and Jupiter, is composed mostly of iron, with some addition of nickel and chromium. So it is most likely that a heavy iron core occupies about one-eighth of the entire volume of our planet and accounts for about one-quarter of its total weight.

Looking at the curve (P) showing the velocity of seismic waves at different depths (Illus. 28), we notice a peculiar kink at the depth of 3100 miles, where what is now known as the outer core ends and the inner core begins. Many students of the Earth's interior attribute that discontinuity to the change from liquid iron in the outer core to solid iron forming the inner core, but one cannot be entirely sure about this assumption.

THE MYSTERY OF THE COMPASS NEEDLE

The existence of the molten iron core of the Earth has an important bearing on the many-centuries-old puzzle of terrestrial magnetism. The great German mathematician Karl Friedrich Gauss has shown that the magnetic field observed on the surface of the Earth can be interpreted as due to a single large magnet placed at the center of the Earth and inclined slightly to its rotation axis. More detailed studies of the magnetic field all over the surface of the Earth have shown, however, that whereas Gauss was right in the first approximation, there are certain deviations from the single-magnet field which are known as residual magnetic fields and which are presumably due to magnetized iron materials in the Earth's solid crust. The pattern of these residual fields drifts westward at such a rate that it will move completely around the Earth in 1600 years. If the main part of the magnetic field is due to the main body of the Earth, and the residual fields to magnetic materials in its crust, this result implies that the solid crust slips eastward over the main body at the rate of about 17 miles per year.

Another evidence for the slipping of the crust in respect to the main body of the Earth is provided by the study of so-called "paleomagnetism," i.e., the magnetic field of the Earth which existed during various past geological eras. Of course, at that time there were no geophysicists, not even men, and the dinosaurs and trilobites were not interested in such problems. But very reliable information can be obtained by studying the magnetism preserved in the rocks which originated at these different eras.

When hot lava containing various iron compounds poured out of the surface of the Earth many millions of years ago, it became magnetized in the direction of the then existing terrestrial magnetic field, and when it solidified its induced magnetism was "frozen" in the North-South direction corresponding to the location of the magnetic poles at that time. When tiny particles resulting from the burning of the incoming meteorites fell into prehistoric lakes and shallow seas, mixing with other materials of the sedimentary layers, they were also magnetized and oriented in that era's North-South direction. Thus, studying the residual magnetism of rocks formed in various locations in different times, we obtain a multitude of tiny "pointing fingers," indicating the North-South direction which existed at that time. Putting all these indications together, we can determine where the magnetic poles were during the various geological eras. The results are shown in Illus. 30, and we see that during the Silurian era the North magnetic pole was somewhere in the vicinity of Japan and moved to its present position during the 300 million years that

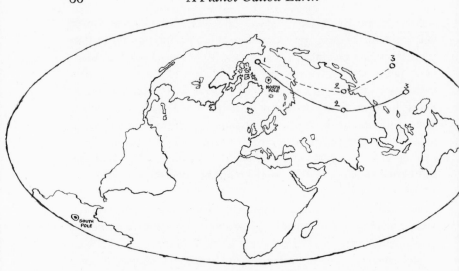

Ill. 30. Motion of the North Magnetic Pole. The solid line indicates positions inferred from American rocks; the broken line, positions inferred from European rocks: 1. present position; 2. position in Triassic times; 3. position in Silurian times.

have passed since that time. The two curves shown in the diagram are based respectively on American and European observations. The fact that these two curves do not coincide may be explained either by inexactness of observations or by the assumption that the two continents moved relative to each other during that period of time.

The problem which is under vital discussion today pertains to the relation between the magnetic field of the Earth and the movements of the molten iron core which is presumably responsible for it. It seems very likely that convective currents in the electrically conductive iron core of the Earth can produce a magnetic field of a proper shape and strength, but the details of that picture are still far from clear.

5

Shaping the Earth's Surface

THE COMMON ROCKS

THE STUDY OF ROCKS on the surface of the Earth shows that the Earth's crust looks very much like the attic of an old house in which broken furniture and all kinds of discarded household effects have been piled up by generations of inhabitants. Geologists are analyzing these piles of debris, and their combined efforts result in a more or less unified picture of the past history of the surface of our planet.

The relative amounts of different minerals forming the Earth's crust are, of course, determined by the relative amounts of various chemical elements which participate in their structure. Illus. 31 shows the percentages of the elements which are most abundant in the crust of the Earth. The two most abundant are oxygen (46.7 per cent) and silicon (27.7 per cent). Thus it is no wonder that the union of these two elements forms a most important compound that participates in the structure of the crustal rocks. A silicon atom united with two oxygen atoms forms a molecule of silicon oxide. These molecules, piling up in a regular pattern, build beautiful crystals of the mineral known as *quartz* (Illus. 32). Chemists denote an atom of silicon by the symbol Si and an atom of oxygen by a symbol O; thus the chemical formula of quartz is SiO_2, the subscript 2 indicating the presence of two atoms of oxygen in each molecule.

The combination of oxygen and silicon with the next most

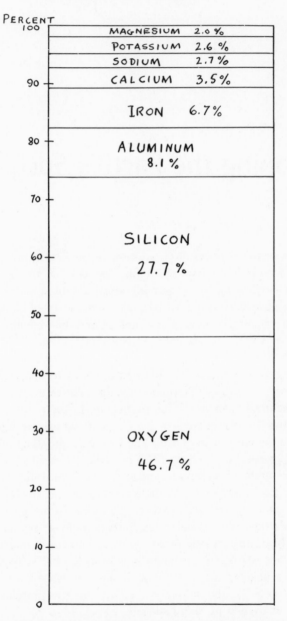

Ill. 31. Relative abundance of chemical elements in the Earth's crust.

Ill. 32. A giant quartz crystal from Madagascar.
(Courtesy of the National Bureau of Standards, Boulder, Colorado)

abundant element, aluminum (chemical symbol *Al*), forms the next most important mineral, known as feldspar (Illus. 33). This trinity of most abundant elements usually invites, to keep them

Ill. 33. Crystals of feldspar.
(Courtesy of R. M. Honea, University of Colorado)

company, the atoms of calcium (Ca), sodium (Na), and potassium (K), forming the compounds:

$$CaAl_2Si_2O_8$$
$$NaAlSi_3O_8$$
$$KAlSi_3O_8$$

which are known to mineralogists as *anorthite*, *albite*, and *orthoclase* respectively.

Of particular importance, also, are the chemical compounds of the previously mentioned elements with magnesium (Mg) and iron (Fe), the most typical of them being *augite*, represented by a cumbersome chemical formula: $Ca(Mg,Fe,Al)$ $(Si,Al)_2O_6$. Because of the great weight of iron atoms, this mineral, as well as other iron compounds, is considerably heavier than the other minerals described.

It is, however, very rarely that a mineralogist finds perfectly shaped large crystals of the "pure" minerals listed above. The ordinary "igneous" rocks, i.e., the rocks solidified from the originally molten material (*igneus* is Greek for "fire"), represent a mixture of microscopically small crystals of various "pure" minerals. Thus granite, the principal material of the continents, consists of

Ill. 34. A photomicrograph of a polished granite surface, showing a
conglomeration of small crystals of various "pure" minerals.
(Courtesy of R. M. Honea, University of Colorado)

about 31 per cent minute quartz crystals, 53 per cent feldspar,
plus small amounts of less abundant minerals such as mica. On the
other hand, the heavier basalt mostly found in the regions of volcanic activity contains practically no quartz, 46 per cent of feldspar, and 40 per cent heavy augite. A microphotograph of a
polished surface of granite is shown in Illus. 34.

An entirely different picture is presented by *sandstone*, which,
when viewed through a lens, is seen to consist of highly compressed grains of sand identical in appearance to those that are
churned up by the waves breaking on the beach. Most of these
grains are tiny polished crystals of quartz, and it is clear that
sandstone is a second-hand material formed chiefly by fragments
of granite which were ground up sometime in the past history of
the Earth's crust and then compressed into solid blocks.

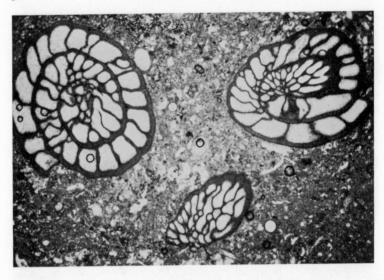

Ill. 35. A photomicrograph of a limestone surface, showing the remnants of ancient shells. *(Courtesy of R. M. Honea, University of Colorado)*

On the other hand, the microscopic examination of *limestone* shows something entirely different. Instead of broken-up crystals of quartz, we find here an accumulation of tiny shells and shell fragments, all of them apparently remnants of the organic life in the seas of past geological eras (Illus. 35). Some limestone contains broken pieces of coral or the stalks of "sea lilies," which are primitive marine animals, related to starfish, and are attached to the bottom rocks on long stalks during part of their lives. There is no doubt that limestone deposits are the cemeteries of primitive marine life of the past, and whenever we use chalk to write on a blackboard, or lime (which is obtained by heating limestone) for our flower gardens, we must be grateful to the tiny marine inhabitants of past eras which provided us with this useful material. Chemically, limestone is composed of calcium carbonate ($CaCO_3$), which is extracted from sea water by primitive marine animals for the construction of protective shells or supporting structures.

Noble *marble* looks rather different from ordinary limestone; marble is much harder, and no microscopic examination can reveal the presence of any microshells or shell fragments. But marble is usually as white as limestone and has exactly the same chemical composition. In fact, geological studies show that the marble used by sculptors is nothing but ordinary limestone which has completely changed its internal texture. If one fills a thick-walled iron container with ordinary chalk powder, seals it, and subjects it to very high temperature, the chalk turns into fine granular marble. Natural marble originates when streams of hot lava come to the surface through the cracks in the Earth's crust and spread over the top of limestone layers. Under the action of heat and weight of overlying lava, the calcium carbonate of the organic remnants becomes completely recrystallized into fine symmetrical grains, and all traces of its organic origin become completely obliterated. Rocks produced by the recrystallization of earlier rocks, caused by high temperature and high pressures, are known as *metamorphic rocks*.

EROSION AND SEDIMENTATION

The variety and diversity of rocks found on the surface of the Earth give vivid evidence of the complexity of the processes which made the face of our planet look as it does today.

There are two principal agents which change continuously but slowly the face of the Earth. One is *tectonic activity*, which has its roots deep under the Earth's surface, and causes all kinds of deformations and crumbling of crustal rocks, piling them on one another to form the mountain ranges (Illus. 36*a* and *b*). The other is *erosion*, which is caused mostly by water and partially by wind, and works in the opposite direction, washing away the mountains and leveling the continental surfaces. If the Earth had no atmosphere and no water, its surface features would preserve, as do those of the Moon, a complete record of its past. As it is, the competition between the tectonic and the erosive processes mixes the existing information in a rather cumbersome way. The old mountains are completely washed away by erosive processes, and the resulting debris is deposited in successive layers at the bottom of shallow inland seas and along the ocean shores (Illus. 36c and d), only to be uplifted again to form new mountains at the next paroxysm of tectonic activity (Illus. 36e and f). The process repeats again and again, making the picture more and more complicated.

The layers of sandstone formed on the ocean bottoms by debris brought from the continents alternate with the layers of limestone

Ill. 36. How the surface of the Earth changes through tectonic activity and erosion.

Ill. 37. Fantastic shapes produced by the action of rain water in the Bad Lands of South Dakota. Note the vertical columns, which remained standing because their material was compressed somewhat more by the weight of the rocks that are seen on top of each column.
(Courtesy of the U.S. Geologic Survey)

produced by the ocean's life, and these deposits are seasoned by the remnants of plants and animals which lived in each era. Then during the next crustal movements these layers of old sediments are uplifted again, high above the ocean level, to form new mountain ranges, and the originally flat layers of old deposits are deformed into giant folds. Those are eroded again and brought back into the ocean, or, in other regions volcanic eruptions cover them with thick layers of igneous rock (see Illus. 36).

A typical example of the erosion process is presented by the Bad Lands of South Dakota (Illus. 37), which have their counter-

95

Ill. 38. The canyon in Yellowstone National Park formed in the volcanic
plateau by the erosive action of the river.

(Courtesy of the U.S. Geologic Survey)

parts in other countries of the world. Under the action of torrential rains, ground not covered by vegetation is carried away,
forming deep troughs. The uneroded material assumes fantastic
shapes, resembling ruins of castle walls and towers, over areas
of thousands of square miles. Other examples of erosion are shown
in Illus. 38.

An interesting result of the process of erosion is the famous
White Sands in the Tularosa Valley of New Mexico. Tularosa
Valley stretches for more than 100 miles, bounded on both sides
by rather steep walls. It was formed hundreds of thousands of
years ago when a long strip of ground sank down because of some
movements of the underlying crustal layers. It is actually a long
ditch, or what geologists call *graben* (German for "grave"). High

above the valley floor beds of gypsum (hydrous calcium sulfate) are found in the mountain slopes flanking it. Similar gypsum beds lie below the valley's floor. A geological cross-section of that region clearly shows how the valley was formed (Illus. 39). During the rainy seasons, water percolates through the mountainsides, dissolves certain amounts of gypsum, comes down into the valley, and forms a "temporary" body of water known as Lake Lucero. During summer periods of cloudless skies, the lake dries out, leaving the gypsum on its dry bottom. Prevailing winds carry the grains of gypsum, often as visible clouds, up the valley, piling it up into large snow-white dunes covering about 275 square miles. The landscape looks like winter in Norway and attracts thousands of tourists.

In such cases as we have described, when the ground water percolates through comparatively easily dissolvable layers, usually limestone, enclosed between two undissolvable layers, long underground passages and caves are formed. One of the biggest known caves of that kind is the famous Carlsbad Caverns in New Mexico, which has a "big room" nearly 4000 feet long, with the walls

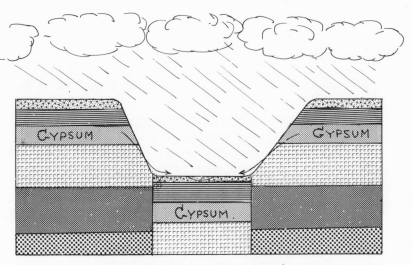

Ill. 39. How White Sands was formed.

over 600 feet apart and the ceiling rising to the height of more than 300 feet.

In addition to the streams which often flow through these underground passages, there is usually a slow leakage of lime-charged water through the tiny cracks in the cave's ceilings. The water in the droplets evaporates and the deposited calcium carbonate forms long "icicles" called *stalactites*, which hang down from the cave's ceiling. Those water droplets that fall to the ground cause the growth of similar structures called *stalagmites*, which rise upward from the floor. These formations are often very beautiful and bizarre and represent the main attraction for visitors.

The guides in the caves always like to give these formations fanciful names, such as "the sitting monkey" and "the Indian's head," to stimulate the tourist's imagination. However, it would be much more exciting to point out that the material forming these structures was produced many millions of years ago as protective shells for marine animals, that it remained for many more millions of years as a compressed sediment at the bottom of an inland sea, and that finally, millions of years ago, it was lifted high above the sea level by primitive forces operating in the interior of the Earth.

UP-AND-DOWN CRUST MOTION

While the possibility that the continents are drifting along the Earth's surface still remains an unsolved problem, we have quite definite information concerning the vertical motions of the Earth's surface. Since, as we have already mentioned, the temperature of the Earth's interior rapidly increases with the depth, some 30 miles under our feet it must reach between 2000 and 3000° F., at which temperature all ordinary rocks will melt; the red-hot lavas which are ejected by volcanoes come from about that depth. But, in contrast to the lava flowing down the slopes of the volcanoes, the material at great depths is subjected not only to very high temperatures but also to tremendously high pressures. In Chapter 4 we have seen that, under these conditions, the rocks do not actually become fluid but attain the property of plasticity, behaving as solid material in respect to fast-acting forces (such as the earthquake waves propagating through the body of our globe), but flowing like honey under the influence of slow but persistent action.

The solid crust of the Earth floats on the plastic layers forming the deeper interiors, very much as polar icefields float on the water below them. This leads to a very important geological phenomenon known by the technical name of *isostasy*. When a large iceberg floats on the surface of the ocean, only a comparatively small part of it protrudes above the water, while most of it is submerged. A similar phenomenon takes place in the case of solid rocks of the Earth's crust which are floating on the plastic material below. To each mountain rising high above the continental plains there corresponds an "anti-mountain" (or mountain root) formed by crustal rocks which are pushed deeper down into the plastic material underneath. And, just as the sunken part of an iceberg is larger than its part protruding above the water, these anti-mountains are probably considerably larger than the mountains which they support above the Earth's surface.

We know that the mountains are not eternal and that their material is slowly eroded and carried away by the rivers. This does not mean, however, that the eroded mountain becomes necessarily lower. In fact, as the weight of the rocks piled above the Earth's surface diminishes, the material of the mountain root slowly floats up, lifting the remaining rocks higher up and maintaining the original height of the mountain. Thus it takes a considerably longer time to wash away a mountain than would appear at first sight.

On the other hand, when a lateral compression of the crust crumples its material and piles it up in the form of a new mountain, a large fraction of the crumbled crustal rocks is pushed deeper into the plastic material below, forming a new mountain root.

Vertical motions of the crust play an important role in shaping the Earth's surface and explain many features which otherwise would be difficult to understand. Take, for example, the Grand

Canyon of the Colorado River, in Arizona, through which the river flows toward the ocean. Suppose that we were able to fill the Grand Canyon, which is now about 6000 feet deep, with rocks up to the rim. What would happen to the Colorado River? Clearly its waters would not flow uphill, the river would have to find some other way to the ocean, and the Grand Canyon would be no more.

Thus, to understand the origin of the Grand Canyon, we have to assume that the high plateau through which it was cut by the Colorado River was once upon a time much lower. And, indeed, geological data indicate that many millions of years ago the area of northern Arizona and southern Utah was a rather low plain with a broad river flowing across it. Then, because of crustal movements, the entire area began to rise higher and higher above sea level, and, as this continued, the river cut deeper and deeper into the surface, washing away more and more material and carrying it into the ocean. Thus the surrounding lands slowly rose higher and higher, while the river bed remained at the same level as it was millions of years ago.

Another even more striking effect of the lifting of the Earth's surface is presented by great rivers crossing the Himalayan mountain ranges. The Indus, originating in the north of Tibet and flowing through Kashmir on its way to the Arabian Sea, passes through narrow deep gorges cut, as if by a saw, through the mountain ranges standing in its way. At Gilgit the river itself is only 3000 feet above its estuary, but the mountains on both sides of it rise nearly 20,000 feet high. The only possible explanation is that the mountain ranges here were much lower in the distant past and that, while the uplift of the grounds was slowly taking place, the river was eroding and carrying away enough material to make a 17,000-foot-deep gorge. The river Arun, a tributary of the Ganges, is 22,000 feet higher than its estuary when passing through a majestic gorge between Everest (29,140 feet) on one side and Kanchenjunga (28,146 feet) on the other. Geological evidence indicates that these two mountains formed in the remote past a continuous ridge and that the passageway must have been made by the river itself. It could not have made this passageway if the mountains had been at the present height, and here again we have to assume that the river was gradually deepening its bed as the surrounding rocks were slowly rising upward.

THE UPLIFTING OF MOUNTAINS

Geologists have long believed that mountains originate as the result of horizontal compression of crustal rocks, which makes them crumble and pile upon one another. What causes this compression? The natural explanation — and the only one until just a few decades ago — was that the compression resulted from the gradual cooling of the Earth. Most materials contract when they are cooled, and so would the body of the Earth. But as the semi-molten interior of the Earth shrinks, the solid outer crust must wrinkle, as does the skin of an apple when it is baked. The mountains, according to this view, are simply the wrinkles of the skin of the gradually cooling Earth.

More recently, another exactly opposite hypothesis appeared to challenge the older views. Everybody knows that a tightly closed bottle filled with water cracks when the water freezes. The glass cracks because the water expands when it turns into ice and its volume increases. Conversely a block of ice decreases in volume when it is heated enough to turn into water. Properties similar to those of ice can be possessed by other materials, and it is not impossible that the rocks forming the interior of the Earth would shrink when they melt and expand when they solidify. This possibility would turn the situation upside down, and in order to explain the shrinkage of the Earth's crust we would have to assume that its interior is gradually heating up so that more and more solid rocks pass into the molten state, thus decreasing in volume.

What could cause such heating of the Earth's interior? The answer is simple: natural radioactivity. We know that the rocks forming the crust of the Earth contain small but noticeable amounts of various radioactive elements which slowly decay, liberating heat. The outer granite layer contains more radioactive materials than the underlying basalt layer, and nobody at present knows why. We also have no idea of the amount of radioactive elements contained in the interior of the Earth. One can calculate, however, that if the entire body of the Earth had the same concentration of radioactive materials as does its crust, the heat produced by their decay would not be able to escape fast enough, and our globe would gradually be heating up. If for some reason radioactive materials were almost absent at the great depths, the reverse would be true and the Earth would be gradually cooling down. Only future studies can decide which of these two possibilities is correct.

Assuming that, for one reason or another, the crust of the Earth is shrinking, we can ask ourselves about the details of mountain formation caused by such a shrinkage. As we stated earlier, the crust of our Earth is far from uniform and consists of large slabs of granite (continental massives) driven into a thinner but denser basalt layer that also forms the bottom of ocean basins. Whenever an object made of two different materials is subjected to the action of applied stress, we would expect it to break along the boundaries separating its different parts. In the case of the Earth's crust, these weak boundaries are the shorelines of the continental massives. It is no wonder therefore that the motion of the Earth's crust produces most noticeable surface crumbling effects along these boundaries. And, indeed, most of the so-called *orogenic belts* (from the Greek *oros*, meaning "mountains") run along the fringes of continental massives. One of them runs all along the shores of the Pacific Ocean, from the Polynesian Islands through Japan, Kamchatka, Alaska, and the western shores of North and South America. Another includes the Alps (and the Atlas Mountains, their counterpart in Africa), the Carpathians, the Caucasus, the Himalayan Mountains, and the mountains of Indonesia, New Guinea and other islands. Most of the earthquakes, volcanic eruptions, and other manifestations of tectonic activity which remind us that we live on a powder barrel occur along these boundaries between continental granite and ocean-bottom basalt.

The situation in the orogenic belts is complicated by the fact that their isostatic conditions are influenced by the sediments brought from the continents and deposited along the shorelines. The weight of these sediments pushes the underlying basalt layers deeper and deeper under the ocean's surface. When the compression of the Earth's crust takes place, the orogenic region, being the weakest section of the crust, bulges up, and the sediments of the past are folded and lifted to make new mountain ranges. And these mountains will stand for tens of millions of years, until persistent rains wash them away and bring their material into the ocean to form new sedimentary layers.

Thus goes the history of the surface of our globe: up and down, up and down, up and down again.

MODEL MOUNTAIN-BUILDING

The mighty tectonic processes which crumble the crust of the Earth occur at an exceedingly slow rate on a scale of many millions of years. Their theoretical interpretation is complicated by the fact that, although the properties of various materials forming the Earth's crust are well known, it is tremendously difficult to analyze the movements of crustal masses even by using modern electronic computers. If a bottle of ink is thrown against a white-washed wall, the shape of the black spot formed is subject to the classical laws of hydrodynamics, but it is quite hopeless to attempt to calculate in advance what that shape will be.

When such complicated problems have to be solved, one may have recourse to making scale models. To find out how a ship which is to be built will behave on its maiden voyage, one builds its model (just a few feet long) and drags it through a long water channel, measuring directly all characteristics which are of importance for its performance. Aeronautical engineers follow exactly the same procedure by testing small models of airplanes or missiles in the wind tunnels. The hydrodynamical or aerodynamical properties of these models can then be "scaled" up to those of the actual craft.

Similarly, the motions of the Earth's crust can be studied on

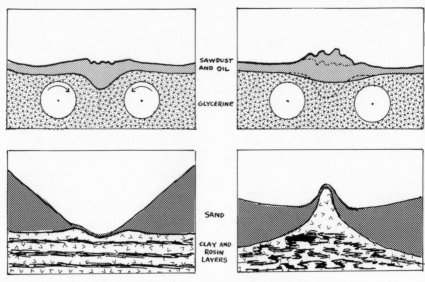

Ill. 40. Models for the study of tectonic processes.

scale models, in which the mechanical properties of the materials used are chosen in such a way that considerable changes can take place in the course of minutes or hours. Geophysicists are beginning to depend more and more on this useful method, which permits them to find within one working day what happens to the crust of the Earth in millions of years. Two of the many different approaches to that problem are illustrated graphically in Illus. 40.

The upper drawings show a model built by an American geophysicist, David Griggs, for the study of crustal motion which can be caused by circular convective currents in the plastic mantle below. It consists of two wooden cylinders rotating in a glycerine medium that represents the plastic material of the Earth's mantle. On the surface of the glycerine floats a lighter layer formed by a mixture of sawdust and oil. When the cylinders are set in motion, the lighter surface material is dragged in, forming a bulge protruding downward. When the rotation of cylinders is stopped (which corresponds to the disappearance of the convective currents in the mantle), the bulge floats up, according to the principle of isostatic equilibrium, and high mountains are formed on that part of the Earth's surface.

The lower drawings show the study of a Russian geophysicist,

V. V. Belousov, who was investigating the possibility of mountain formation as the result of uneven distribution of mass on the Earth's surface. In this experiment alternating levels of soft clay and rosin were subjected to the weight of two piles of sand. In a rather short time a very large deformation of the originally flat surface occurred: a tall bulge appeared at the center and the layers of rosin were folded in a manner similar to the folding of rocks often encountered in mountainous regions. This shows that, even though such experiments at first sight seem like "reading tea leaves" (or *cofainaya guschcha* — coffee-grounds — in Russian), they can give us a reasonably good understanding of the tectonic processes which shape the surface of the Earth.

UNDERWATER MOUNTAINS

When, in the year 1873, the good British ship *Challenger* sailed away on its epoch-making three-and-a-half-year around-the-world voyage for the study of the oceans, one of its main tasks was the measurement of the ocean's depth along its long and winding course. At that time the method of depth-measurement was very rudimentary and tedious: one simply lowered a heavy lead weight on a long hemp line marked at equal intervals, so that the depth was known as soon as the lead struck the bottom.

It was expected that, beyond the continental shelves formed by debris brought into the oceans from the land, the ocean floor would be reasonably flat. However, the scientists aboard the *Challenger* found an entirely different picture. It turned out that, while on the European and American sides of the Atlantic Ocean the depth was about 2000 fathoms (12,000 feet), in the middle part of the ocean, the depth was not more than 1000 fathoms. This discovery gave temporary support to the ancient legend that thousands of years ago there existed a continent called Atlantis, which later sank under the surface of the water.

Nowadays we have a much better and faster method for measuring the ocean's depth, based on the "sonar" techniques developed during the Second World War for the detection of enemy

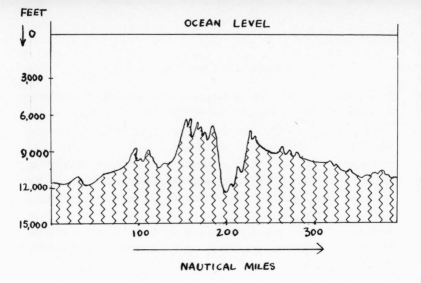

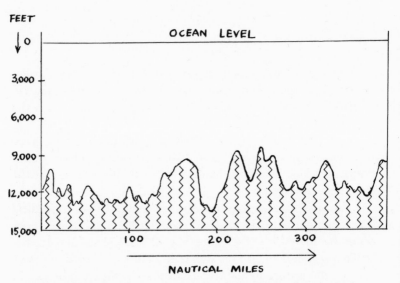

Ill. 41. The mid-Atlantic ridge (top) and the Arctic ridge (bottom).

submarines. While a ship is sailing at full speed along its course, high-frequency sound waves, emitted by an echo sounder attached to the hull, are reflected from the ocean bottom, and the delay of the echo is measured by sensitive instruments. This permits a rapid and exact survey of the profile of the bottom along the ship's course.

106

Using this method, one finds that the mid-Atlantic ridge has a very peculiar shape, rising 5000 or 6000 feet above the ocean's bottom on its eastern and western sides and possessing a deep trough running along its "spine" (Illus. 41, top). This ridge runs through the South and North Atlantic oceans, about halfway between the Old and the New World, and continues into the Arctic Ocean, passing close to the North Pole and ending at eastern Siberia. Illus. 41, bottom, shows the profile of that ridge and trough in the Arctic Ocean as obtained by the United States Navy atomic submarine *Nautilus* during her famous voyage under the Arctic icefields.

In recent years world-wide studies of the ocean bottom by oceanographic ships of various nations have revealed that the mid-Atlantic ridge is just a part of a much larger and more complicated system running through all the oceans of the globe (Illus. 42) and covering a submerged area comparable to the combined area of all continents. It is interesting to notice that these submarine features are correlated with the familiar features of the dry lands. Thus the ridge and trough running along the western

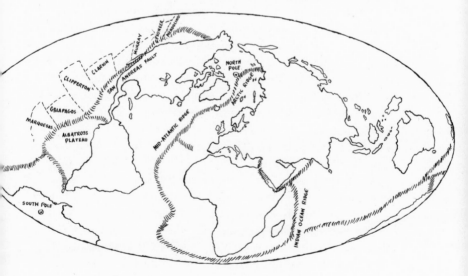

Ill. 42. The underwater mountain ranges.

shores of North and South America seem to be responsible for the existence of the Gulf of California in the north and the Strait of Magellan in the south. The mid-Atlantic rift passes right through Iceland and may be responsible for a large crack (or *gjá*) crossing that island in a north-south direction. Similarly, the Indian Ocean ridge and trough has its continuation as the Gulf of Aden and the Red Sea, with the possibility that its inland continuation is responsible for the existence of Lakes Victoria, Tanganyika, and Nyasa in eastern Africa.

The structure of the submerged mountain ranges appears to be quite different from that of such familiar surface ranges as the Rockies or the Alps. Whereas in the latter case the uplift of the ground is clearly caused by sidewise compression that turned the originally horizontal rock levels into giant folds, the submarine mountains seem more likely to be the result of horizontal stresses that caused rifting, and both sides of the rift having been lifted upward by the pressure of the plastic material from below. The assumption of a rift would explain the presence of deep troughs running along the length of the submarine ridges, a feature never observed in the case of continental mountain ranges. An important fact in favor of the rift hypothesis is that most of the submarine earthquakes have their epicenters located along the troughs of the submarine mountain ranges and may be due to the intrusion into the ocean water of hot lava through the cracks in the bottom (or to the intrusion of the ocean water through the cracks into the hot lava below). The stretching of the ocean floors and the squeezing of the continents is ascribed by many geophysicists to the convective currents in the semi-molten (plastic) mantle of the Earth, but so far no definite proof of that hypothesis has been given.

Another puzzling fact concerning the behavior of the ocean floor was recently disclosed by the studies of Scripps Oceanographic Institution, and pertains to the horizontal displacements of the bottom rocks. It seems that the giant slabs of the ocean floor near the western shore of the Americas are being shifted in an east-west direction in respect to one another (Illus. 42). The cause of these displacements is still unknown.

To sum up, one can say that the exploration of the ocean's floor during the last few decades presents opportunities comparable with those which existed during the early exploration of the dry surface of the Earth. The advantage of the study of the underwater mountains as compared with that of the mountains above the surface is that the former are presumably much better preserved. As we have already seen, the mountains rising above the surface of the continents are subject to continuous erosion as the result of periodic temperature changes, winds, and rains. At the bottom of the ocean the temperature remains nearly constant, there are of course no winds, and, although there is plenty of water, it never rains. The slow circulation of the ocean water along the bottom can hardly be expected to erode the high rocky ridges. Thus the underwater landscape is expected to remain almost as permanent as that of the Moon, and its detailed study may give us much valuable information concerning the past history of our globe.

THE BOOK OF SEDIMENTS

During billions of years, the surface features of the continents have undergone continuous transformation, owing to the combined action of the mountain-raising forces and the destructive action of rain. This periodic formation of mountain chains and their subsequent destruction by water are clearly shown by the character of the deposits of eroded material carried into the seas by the rivers of the past. In fact, the nature of such deposits depends to a large extent on the character of the surface that is being eroded.

During the revolutionary periods, such as the one that we are living in now, high mountains rise everywhere on the surface of the continents, and erosion proceeds very fast. Rapid streams rushing down steep mountain slopes break off comparatively large pieces of rock by purely mechanical action, and the deposits formed during these periods consist mainly of rather rough materials, such as gravel and coarse sand. On the other hand, during

the long inter-revolutionary epochs, when most of the mountains
are already washed away completely, and the surface of the continents is level and dull, the process of erosion necessarily slows
down. There are no rushing mountain streams, no noisy water-
falls, and the rainwater that continues to fall on the Earth's surface is drained into the oceans and seas by broad, slow rivers
running across low, almost horizontal plains. During these long
periods, chemical erosion is more effective than purely mechanical disintegration.

Water, slowly moving across the surface of the Earth, carries
into solution various soluble parts of the rocks, leaving fine sand
and clay as the residue. The dissolved material is mostly calcium
carbonate, which is carried out into the seas and deposited as
thick layers of limestone.

Thus, if we were able to examine some spots on the Earth
where the formation of sedimentary deposits has been going on
uninterruptedly throughout the geologic history of our planet, a
cross-section of the deposits would look very regular. We would
find periodic repetitions of fine and coarse material, corresponding
to the revolutionary and inter-revolutionary epochs, and we would
be able to reconstruct the entire history of our planet chapter by
chapter. Such a complete edition of the "Book of Sediments"
undoubtedly exists on the bottoms of the oceans along the continental shorelines, since, being continuously submerged, these
areas have been receiving an uninterrupted flow of eroded material from the nearby lands. Deep-sea drillings such as Project
Mohole (see Chapter 4) hold promise of producing very valuable
information about the past history of the earth, but our present
knowledge is derived entirely from the study of the deposits
formed in the intracontinental shallow seas and brought up to the
surface of the Earth by the subsequent elevation of the ground
and the erosion of the layers lying above.

Since the surface of the continents has been moving up and
down irregularly throughout the Earth's history, and the interior
seas have always been changing their sites, the records contained
in the sediments left at any one place are necessarily incomplete.
In Illus. 43 we give a schematic picture of what we can expect

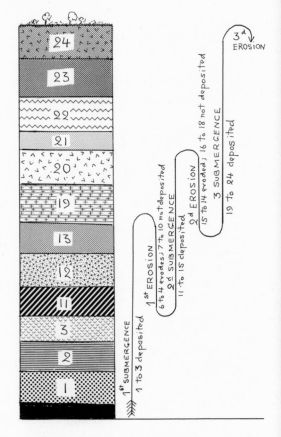

Ill. 43. How periodic elevations of the ground spoil the continuity of geological records.

to find at a spot that was subject to three submergences, but now is on dry land. Let us suppose that during the first submergence period the deposits carried down by the rivers formed six successive layers, which we distinguish by the numbers 1 to 6.* Suppose now that after these layers, representing a continuous record of the corresponding interval of the Earth's history, were formed, movements of the crust elevated this particular locality above sea level, so that the newly formed layers were exposed to the destructive action of rainwater. During the period of elevation part of the sedimentary layers was carried away by erosion, and this material, mixed with material taken from other places, was de-

---

* The enumeration of the layers used here does not correspond to any real division of geologic time and is used only for convenience in discussion.

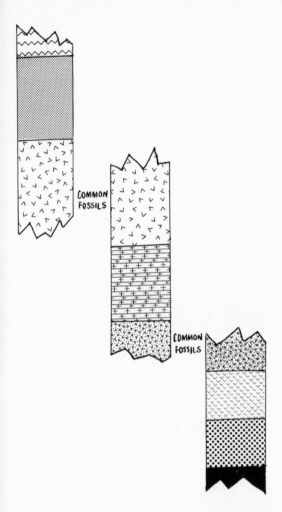

COMMON
FOSSILS

COMMON
FOSSILS

Ill. 44. Putting together discon-
nected fragments of the "Book
of Sediments."

posited elsewhere. While new sedimentary layers (let us say 7, 8, 9, and 10) were being formed on the bottom of the ocean, where the deposits were accumulating continuously, our locality was only losing its material, the three upper layers (6, 5, and 4) being completely removed. Thus, when the new submergence occurred, layer 11 began to be deposited directly on top of old layer 3.

Inspecting Illus. 43 further, we find that the only sedimentary layers left in this hypothetical locality and presenting themselves to the hammer of the geologist are those numbered 1, 2, 3, 11, 12,

13, 19, 20, 21, 22, 23, 24, while all the others were never formed or were eroded by rainwater.

But though the layers deposited in any given locality represent only a collection of disunited occasional pages of the "Book of Sediments," we can try to reconstruct the complete copy of the book by comparing the findings in a number of places that were submerged at different times. This task is, of course, a very difficult one, and work in this field represents the main subject of historical geology. The principal method used in the reconstruction of the complete "geological column" from the disunited fragments is based on the "principle of overlapping" explained schematically in Illus. 44. It may happen that, comparing two separate fragments corresponding to the uninterrupted sedimentation process in different localities, we notice that the upper layers of one fragment are of the same nature as the lower layers of another. If such is the case, the conclusion is inevitable that the layers at the top of the first fragment were being formed simultaneously with the bottom layers of the second; putting the two fragments together so that the layers corresponding to the same time overlap, we get a continuous record covering the larger time interval.*

---

* A similar method of overlapping is very successfully used in studying prehistoric Indian villages in different parts of North America. Since such villages were mostly situated on the lake shore, one finds at the bottoms of these lakes a large number of petrified logs that once formed the village buildings. Now, it is known that the pattern of vegetation rings in the cross-section of a tree trunk is just as characteristic of the time interval during which the tree was growing as the fingerprint of a man, and depends upon the climatic conditions during the life span of the tree. In fact, during warm summers with plenty of rain the corresponding annual rings will grow thicker, whereas very thin rings will correspond to dry summers. Thus, if one finds two logs in which the patterns of annual rings partly overlap, one can be sure that the two trees were growing at the same time (corresponding to the period of overlap). Putting together a large number of logs, selected in such a way that the outer rings of each (i.e., the rings formed shortly before the tree was cut down) coincide with more central rings on the next one, it is possible to build a continuous "tree column" covering an interval of many centuries. From this column we can get exact information as to the dates when different logs were cut down for construction purposes. What is most interesting, we can also get a rough meteorological record of the climatic changes in this particular locality over a period of time during which the word "meteorology" itself was unknown.

It must be borne in mind, however, that since the differences between purely physical and chemical characteristics of various deposits are not very large, and since the same kinds of deposits repeat periodically in time, the method of overlapping described would not yield much in the way of results if the sedimentary layer did not contain the fossilized remainders of different plants and animals living during the corresponding

Ill. 45. Geologic time chart.

epochs. In fact, the development of historical geology is insep-
arably connected with the development of paleontology (i.e., the
science of ancient life); together with the complete geological
column representing the history of land and sea, we also get the
complete record of the evolution of life.

The work of collecting the fragmentary pages of the Earth's
history here and there and binding them together into one con-

(Courtesy of the University of Colorado Museum)

sistent volume must, of course, become increasingly difficult as we go back to more and more remote epochs. Thus, while the later parts of the "Book of Sediments" are fairly complete by now, the records of earlier periods are still in a very imperfect state. Classification of these early pages of the book becomes particularly difficult because at the time they were "written" life on the Earth either did not exist at all or was limited to the simplest organisms, which left no trace in the sediments of that time.

The completed "Book of Sediments" still possessed one essential defect: it completely lacked any chronology, and though we could say that one layer was formed after or before another, we had no idea of the period of time separating them. In order to get the "timing" of geological events, very elaborate but uncertain speculations about the deposition rates of different types of materials had always been necessary, and it is therefore very fortunate that the discovery of radioactivity gave us a much simpler and much more exact method of establishing a geologic time scale.

In Chapter 1 we described in some detail how a fairly good idea of the time when different igneous rocks solidified is obtained by studying the relative amounts of the disintegration products of uranium and thorium contained in them. Applying this method to the rocks formed by volcanic eruptions in the past and found now and then in different sedimentary layers, we can add the last touch to the "Book of Sediments" by marking on each page the approximate date at which it was "written."

Illus. 45 gives the general picture of the evolution of the Earth's surface, indicating the names of different eras and periods, the successive processes of mountain formation, and the prevailing types of plants and animals. On the extreme right is shown the absolute time scale as given by the "radioactive clock."

CHAPTERS AND PARAGRAPHS OF THE "BOOK OF SEDIMENTS"

The "Book of Sediments," as reconstructed by the work of generations of geologists, certainly represents a most extensive historic document, alongside which all the thick volumes of the history of the human race are no more than an insignificant booklet. The layer eroded from continental surfaces by rainwater is, on the average, more than a mile thick. Since, however, these disintegration products are mostly deposited in comparatively small areas along the shores, the actual thickness of the geologic column is considerably greater. Putting together all the fragmented pieces of this column, we obtain a total thickness of about 60 miles, each year corresponding to a layer about 0.04 inch thick. *If we consider a year's deposit as one "page" of the "Book of Sediments," such a page will be comparable in thickness with a page in any ordinary book. The reconstructed part of the "book" will have about two billion pages, covering the same number of years of the Earth's history.* This thickness, however, corresponds only to the later part of the evolution of the surface of our planet, and there are billions of earlier fragmented pages that are still largely hidden under the surface. Pursuing our analogy with the ordinary book, we must bear in mind, of course, that one page of the "Earth book" does not record much of its history, and that in order to notice any changes one must thumb through at least several hundred thousand pages. This is also true of the book of human history; whereas the year-to-year changes may have been of special interest to the persons living during these epochs, considerably longer periods of time are needed to manifest any interesting changes in the evolution of humanity.

The first important feature of the "Book of Sediments" is that, like any other book, it is divided into a number of separate chapters corresponding to the revolutionary epochs of mountain-building and the intermediate long periods of submergence previously discussed. It is very hard to say how many chapters there are in the "book," since its earliest parts are still in a very fragmentary and incomplete state; only the last three chapters, covering the last 600,000,000 years, tell a more or less complete and consistent story. These last three chapters represent about one-eighth of the total life span of our planet and are of particular interest, since, as we have indicated, they cover practically the entire period during which life has left its record in fossils on our planet. The three periods of time described in these last three chapters are known as the *Early Paleozoic, Late Paleozoic,* and *Mesozoic* eras of the Earth's history. Finally, at the very end of the "book," we find the beginning of the new *Cenozoic* chapter, which commenced just recently. In geologic language the expression "just recently" means "about seventy million years ago" and is completely justified by the fact that this period of time is very short indeed, compared with the average length of each chapter, which covers between one and two hundred million years. Besides the natural division of the Earth's history into a number of chapters, each starting with a revolutionary epoch of mountain formation, geologists divide the separate chapter into a number of smaller paragraphs. Thus, the early part of the Paleozoic chapter is divided into the *Cambrian, Ordovician,* and *Silurian* periods, whereas the subdivisions of the Mesozoic chapter are known as the *Triassic, Jurassic,* and *Cretaceous* periods. Such subdivisions are entirely arbitrary and are based on the fact that different parts of the geologic column were originally studied in different localities. For example, strata of Cambrian rock were first discovered and studied in Wales, and the period was therefore named for "Cambria," which is the Latin name for ancient Wales; the name "Jurassic" similarly refers to deposits first found in the Jura Mountains between France and Switzerland. Since there are no natural grounds for the further subdivision of geologic time, however, this terminology can be retained simply for the sake of convenience.

In the following sections we give a short account of the major happenings during these different periods of the Earth's history.

THE EARLIEST FRAGMENTED PAGES

The very first pages of the "Book of Sediments" must, of course, date back to the day when the first drop of rain fell from the sky on the cooled surface of our planet, and the first crack started its destructive work on the primeval granite crust. Most of the deposits corresponding to this early epoch are hidden deep in the Earth and come to the surface in only a very few places.

This early extensive period of sedimentation was evidently followed two billion years ago by the revolutionary crumpling of the Earth's crust known as the *Laurentian revolution*,* during which large masses of molten granite were poured over these layers, while the layers themselves were uplifted and folded into giant mountains. It is useless, of course, to look for these mountains on present-day geographical maps, for they were completely obliterated by the action of rainwater many hundreds of millions of years ago. Since the deposits of that distant past can now be found in only a few places on the surface of the Earth (for example, in eastern Canada), it is altogether impossible to form any idea of the geographical distribution of these early mountains from their remaining roots.

After the erosion of the first recorded mountain chains, large areas of the continents were again covered by water, and thick layers of new deposits were formed on top of the previous ones. Then another revolution (the *Algoman*) ensued, accompanied by new mountain-formation processes and new intrusions of granite lavas, again followed by a long quiet sedimentation period. Then again a revolution and still another sedimentation. . . .

But the reader is probably growing tired of this constant repetition of the words "revolution" and "sedimentation"; to cheer him up we can tell him that there will be some more color to the picture after one more repetition. In fact, beginning with the fifth recorded revolution, known as the *Charnian*, we leave the dark prehistoric periods of the Earth's life and enter the epoch comparable to that of ancient Egypt in the history of humanity. The sedimentary layers formed during the epochs following the Charnian revolution have been studied in many places on the Earth; they give us a rather complete picture of the evolution of its surface. Besides, they begin to contain the fossils of different primitive animals in steadily increasing numbers, which is of great help in establishing the "page sequence" in the book of the Earth's

---

* It must be remembered that this revolution need not have been the first one to take place on the surface of the Earth. In fact, there probably were many earlier outbursts of tectonic activity, but since the "Book of Sediments" was not yet in existence at the time, we have no way of judging them.

history. The deposits formed after the Charnian revolution represent three complete chapters of the "Book of Sediments," and on
top of them we find the comparatively thin layers constituting the
beginning of the latest chapter, in the writing of which we have
the pleasure of participating ourselves.

THREE COMPLETE CHAPTERS OF THE "BOOK OF SEDIMENTS"

As a result of the Charnian revolution, which opens the historical era of the Earth's existence, all the continents were lifted
high above sea level, and they were probably considerably larger
in extent than they are today. In North America, for example, this
general uplift caused the Atlantic and the Pacific to recede so that
dry land extended many hundreds of miles into the regions now
covered by the oceans. The present basins of the Gulf of Mexico
and the Caribbean Sea were also occupied by land, while both
the Americas, now united only by a narrow isthmus, formed one
continuous continent, as indicated in the first map of our cinema-
tographic history of North America (Illus. 48 to 55). On the
other side of the Atlantic the continents also protruded much
farther west than they do now; in particular a long string of land
known as "Atlantida"* reached out from the British Isles toward
Greenland.

But, as after all the previous revolutions, the uplifted continents
slowly began to sink back into the plastic mass below, and the
incessant pounding of the rain washed away the rocky material of
the mountains and high plateaus. Ocean water crept inland and,
covering the lower parts of continents, formed numerous inland
seas. On the continent of Eurasia, the waters of the ocean, penetrating deep into the interior, formed an extensive inland basin
covering all the area now occupied by Germany, southern Russia,
the southern part of Siberia, and most of China. This large inland

---

* This land, of course, has nothing to do with the mythical "Atlantis" of the
ancients, since it existed hundreds of millions of years before man appeared
on the surface of the Earth.

sea was surrounded by a ring of highlands passing through the present positions of Scotland, Scandinavia, northern Siberia, the Himalayas, the Causasus, the Balkans, and the Alps.* The continent of Africa, however, seems to have been completely out of the water during all that time, and it was connected with Europe by dry land extending over the present Mediterranean basin. The northern part of Australia was submerged by the waters of the Indian Ocean, whereas its southern part extended much farther south toward the Antarctic. On this side of the Atlantic, the advance of the ocean in the equatorial region almost split the American continent in two (North and South America), and much of what is now Mexico and Texas was also inundated. The waters of the North Pacific covered most of the central area of North America, including the entire Mississippi Valley, the region of the Great Lakes, and part of southern Canada. South of the equator, the advancing Atlantic waters formed an extensive shallow sea covering most of what is now Brazil.

Although this extensive inundation was the most characteristic feature of the Early Paleozoic chapter of the Earth's history and lasted for about 160 million years, one must not think that this epoch was completely devoid of movements of the crust. There are, in fact, some traces of minor mountain-formation activity, and the slow elevations and sinkings taking place in the continental areas were causing the inland seas to change the shape of their shorelines continuously. But all these changes were on a minor scale, and the stresses in the crust were slowly gathering their forces for the major outbreak that finally took place in the year 280,000,000 B.C.

The great disturbances of the Earth's crust that opened the next, the Late Paleozoic, chapter of the "Book of Sediments" are known as the *Caledonian revolution*, the name being derived from the mountains of the same name in Scotland and northern Ireland, where the results of the revolution were particularly pro-

---

* It must be remembered that these elevations were completely obliterated long ago by erosion; the mountains now rising in these regions are of considerably later formation.

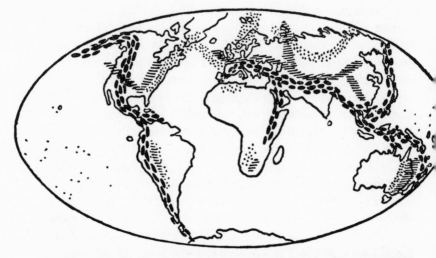

Ill. 46. Three great mountain-folding revolutions of the last 300,000,000 years: 1. mountain chains of the Caledonian revolution (about 320,000,000 B.C.), represented by small dots; 2. mountain chains of the Appalachian revolution (about 200,000,000 B.C.), represented by thin lines; 3. mountain chains of the Laramide revolution (between 70,000,000 and 35,000,000 B.C.), represented by large dots.

nounced. As the result of this revolution, a large mountain chain was elevated along a line running through Scotland, the North Sea, and the Scandinavian peninsula up to Spitsbergen.

The extension of this chain ran across northern Siberia and formed the elevated northern border of the Asiatic continent. Another mountain chain extended from Scotland through the North Atlantic all the way to Greenland, completely separating the Arctic Ocean from the waters of the North Atlantic. In North America, where the revolutionary activity began somewhat later than in Eurasia, high mountain ranges were raised along a line running from the eastern extremity of Canada through Nova Scotia and continuing farther south along the Atlantic coast. There was also very pronounced activity at many points in South America, South Africa, and Australia, as can be seen from the map of Illus. 46, which shows the major accomplishments of the Caledonian revolution.

In spite of all this large-scale mountain-folding activity, the Caledonian revolution apparently was far from being as intensive as the previous one, and the general upheaval of land was considerably less pronounced. In fact, whereas the waters were completely forced away from the continental surfaces during the Charnian revolution, the Caledonian uplift left the Central North American Sea almost untouched, together with the large water basin of Central and Eastern Europe. Another indication of the comparative mildness of the Caledonian revolution is the fact that it evidently did not relieve the stress in the Earth's crust entirely, since we find rather pronounced activity of the crust through the entire Late Paleozoic chapter. There were countless small elevations and sinkings of land and the formation of various small mountain chains throughout the 130 million years that separated the Caledonian from the subsequent Appalachian revolution.

This revolution, which opens the Mesozoic chapter, culminated the crust movements that had been continuing on a minor scale all through the previous period of submergence and raised a number of high mountain chains all over the world (Illus. 27).

In North America, the folding of the crust formed a V-shaped mountain system with its apex in Texas. One branch of this system extended along the Gulf Coast and all along the present site of the Appalachian Mountains, while another branch ran northwest, forming the ancestral Rockies and extending all the way to Puget Sound. In Europe, the compression of the crust formed a long chain beginning somewhere in Ireland (or farther out in the Atlantic), running through central France and southern Germany, and probably joining the Asian mountain chain north of the present site of the Himalayas.

Like all the other mountains of the past, these once magnificent chains were long ago obliterated by rain, and the fact that some of these areas are at present slightly elevated above the continental plains is due to much later upheavals. The present Appalachians, from which the name of the revolution itself is derived, and the Vosges and Sudeten Mountains, represent but poor reminders of the glory of the year 200,000,000 B.C.

The Mesozoic submergence period, lasting down to the most

recent revolution, which took place only 70 million years ago, is in many respects analogous to the previous periods of submergence. Countless lowlands, marshes, and shallow seas provided vast playgrounds for the giant lizards that dominated the animal world of that time.

But the stresses in the crust were gathering new strength, and the Earth was preparing for its latest revolution, which gave its surface its present aspect.

THE BEGINNING OF THE MOST RECENT CHAPTER

As we have said, the latest mountain-building epoch, known as the *Laramide revolution*, began about 70 million years ago and, according to all indications, is still going on at the present time. The fact that we live in a revolutionary period should not lead us to expect to see new mountains rising from the Earth every day like mushrooms! As we have seen, all the processes in the Earth's crust take place extremely slowly, and it is quite possible that all the earthquakes and volcanic activity occurring throughout the recorded history of the human race represent preparations for the next major catastrophe, which will result in the formation of new chains in some unexpected place. The evidence forcing us to assume that the activities of the Laramide revolution are still far from concluded is based on the fact that everything accomplished by this latest revolution up to now (i.e., the Rockies, the Alps, the Andes, the Himalayas, etc.) is still considerably short of the achievements of any of the previous ones. Though "our" revolution may simply be not so world-shaking as past revolutions were, it seems more reasonable to assume merely that it has not reached its peak as yet.

Nearly all the mountains now existing on the surface of the Earth were raised up by this last revolution, and if our conclusion that this revolution is not yet completed is true, more mountain chains are bound to be formed in the "immediate future" (in the geological sense of the word, of course).

The last 70 million years, representing the beginning of the Cenozoic chapter, are arbitrarily divided into six consecutive paragraphs known as: Paleocene, Eocene, Oligocene, Miocene, Pliocene, and Pleistocene periods.* The latest of these periods began in the great epoch of glaciation that we shall discuss in the next chapter, and it continues down to the present time.

One of the first great achievements of the Laramide revolution (Illus. 46) was the giant crumpling of the crust in the southern part of Asia, which raised the brand-new mountains of the Himalayas high above the surrounding plains. This crumpling was accompanied by terrific volcanic activity, and unprecedented quantities of basaltic lava were spread over the surrounding regions. The Deccan plateau, for example, which includes a large part of the Indian peninsula, rests upon basaltic rocks 10,000 feet thick, the cooled-down lava poured over the surface of the Earth during this period of upheaval.

Another giant eruption of subterranean material also occurred in Japan at about the same time.

On this side of the Atlantic, the compression of the crust during the early part of the Laramide revolution (in the Paleocene period) raised a giant mountain chain running almost from pole to pole and now known as the Rockies in North America and the Andes south of the equator. The folding of the major American mountain system was also accompanied by volcanic activity, second only to the Indian instance we have mentioned; the layers of erupted lava, in some places several thousand feet deep, formed the extensive Columbia plateau in the states of Washington and Oregon.

These great events of the "first days" of the revolution evidently relieved the stress in the crust somewhat, and the Eocene and Oligocene periods were characterized by comparative quiescence and the lowering of the land elevated previously. But during the following Miocene period, only about 20 million years after the first outbreak, the revolutionary activity was resumed. The land

---

* The first five periods are often united under the general name of "Tertiary" and the latest one is then called the "Quaternary" period. In some classifications the Paleocene epoch is included in the Mesozoic era.

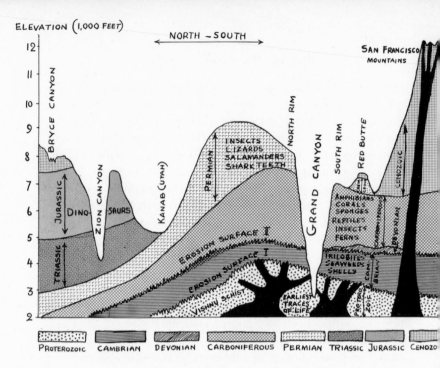

ELEVATION (1,000 FEET)

NORTH – SOUTH

Ill. 47. A highly schematic cross-section of the Earth's crust through the Grand, Zion, and Bryce Canyons. The vertical scale is about sixty times larger than the horizontal scale.

was again elevated considerably, pushing back the ocean waters that had managed to creep up on it during the period of quiescence, and new mountain folds, including the Alps in Europe and the Cascade Range in North America, were formed on the surface of our planet. This second outburst of the revolution continued on a somewhat smaller scale during the subsequent Pliocene period, and is still continuing at the present time.

DRIVING THROUGH THE EARTH'S HISTORY

A vivid impression of the Earth's past can be obtained by a comparatively short uphill and downhill drive through the National Parks and Monuments in northern Arizona and southern Utah (Illus. 47). This region of the North American continent underwent a series of alternating upheavals and depressions during the course of geological history, and deep canyons were cut in it by the Colorado River and its local tributaries.

Arriving at the south rim of the Grand Canyon, which is about 7000 feet above sea level, the motorist will be stopped by an impressive ditch 4500 feet deep and 10 miles wide. To proceed further north, one must change from a comfortable automobile seat to a shaky saddle on the back of a mule that carefully makes its way along the narrow path leading to the floor of the canyon. Down at the bottom one encounters the rushing yellow-brownish waters of the Colorado River, which is responsible for digging the ditch in the slowly rising Arizona-Utah plateau. The speed of the turbulent river varies from 3 to 10 miles per hour. Its width in some places is over 300 feet, and its depth varies from 12 to 45 feet. It was estimated that the Colorado River carries in this part of its course nearly a million tons of sand and silt every day. The particles of solid materials act as sandpaper on the bottom of the river, and slowly dig its bed deeper and deeper into the solid rock below.

Standing on the suspension bridge which crosses the Colorado River, one is surrounded by almost vertical walls rising up about 1500 feet. The walls are formed by ancient sedimentary rocks known as Vishnu schist, penetrated by thick veins of granite, which earned that part of the canyon the name Granite Gorge. Early in the Proterozoic era, more than 700 million years ago, this part of the continent was submerged below sea level, and thick deposits of sandstone and limestone were formed. These deposits show the earliest traces of life on our globe. Later on, lateral compression of the crust folded these layers into mighty mountains, and the masses of molten granite from below were squeezed upward through the cracks in the broken sedimentary rocks. Still later, the erosion obliterated the mountains, turning the region into a flat volcanic plateau which ultimately sank down below sea level.

About 1000 feet of sedimentary rocks deposited on the top of this first erosion surface belong to the Cambrian period. They contain innumerable fossils of seaweeds, miniature shells, early snail-like animals, and trilobites, similar to horseshoe crabs, which, because of their large size (up to three inches) were the undisputed rulers of that time.

The next two periods — Ordovician and Silurian — which are evidenced in other regions of our globe are completely absent in the Grand Canyon records, and only traces of Devonian era deposits are present. Apparently either, during these three geological eras covering about 150 million years, the Arizona-Utah region was elevated above sea level so that no deposits could be formed, or, if any sea deposits were formed during that period, they were washed away during the following millions of years, when this region was uplifted again. Thus, after the second discontinuation in the records, we run right into the Carboniferous period, during which over 2000 feet of deposits were formed. Practical-minded prospectors call these formations blue lime, while scientifically minded geologists prefer the name Redwall limestone. Well, is it blue or red? To tell the truth, the prospectors are in this case more correct than the geologists. The rocks forming the Great Redwall of the Grand Canyon are actually grayish-blue limestone, but their exposed surface is stained bright red by iron oxides brought by rainwater from the upper layers. In any case, a visitor to the Grand Canyon will see the Great Redwall stretching across its mighty chest just like a red ribbon on the chest of a general from a Vienna operetta. This Carboniferous red ribbon is rich in life records of that period: it contains numerous fossilized fernlike plants, corals and sponges, as well as the footprints of primitive amphibians and reptiles.

Finally, to make a long story short, we mention the Permian deposits covering the north rim of the Grand Canyon, which contain a wealth of information concerning the flora and fauna of that period. Plant life was represented principally by ferns and small cone-bearing shrubs or trees of over thirty different species, many of which have not been found anywhere else in the world. Animal life is evidenced by the trails of ancient worms, insect wings (up to 4 inches long), and the footprints of early lizard- or salamander-like creatures, most of them five-toed and several inches in length. Occasional shark teeth found here indicate that this region was also once upon a time wholly submerged below the ocean level.

Driving north from the Grand Canyon (either by crossing it on the back of a mule or by making a detour of over 200 miles), after passing through the pleasant little town of Kanab, the motorist will arrive at Zion Canyon. While most visitors look on the Grand Canyon from above (at either of its two rims), Zion Canyon is to be looked upon from below. And, standing on the shore of the tiny and quiet Virgin River running through it, one finds it hard to believe that this river has excavated such a deep and wide ditch. The rocks forming the walls of Zion Canyon are considerably younger than those of the Grand Canyon, belonging to the Triassic and the Jurassic periods of the Mesozoic era. Geologists find abundant evidence of crocodile-like reptiles, giant amphibians, and dinosaurs which must have inhabited this area some 100 million years ago, when it probably was the shoreline of some inland lake or river and enjoyed a subtropical climate. A short drive from the Zion Lodge brings the visitor to the still younger region at Bryce Canyon, which is formed by the deposits of the Cenozoic era. Here again we look down from above and see an impressive picture of erosion similar to but more colorful than the Bad Lands of South Dakota.

To complete the description of geological formations in the Grand Canyon region, one must mention the Red Butte formed from cretaceous deposits protected from the erosion by a heavy Cenozoic cap, and the San Francisco Mountains, formed by volcanic eruptions during the Cenozoic era.

Solidly indoctrinated with the secrets of the Earth's past, the traveler may now proceed to Las Vegas, Nevada, for less intellectual kinds of entertainment.

CINEMATOGRAPHIC HISTORY OF NORTH AMERICA

In the foregoing sections we have given a brief abstract of the history of the continents as it can be read in the "Book of Sediments." Naturally enough, we had to confine ourselves to the

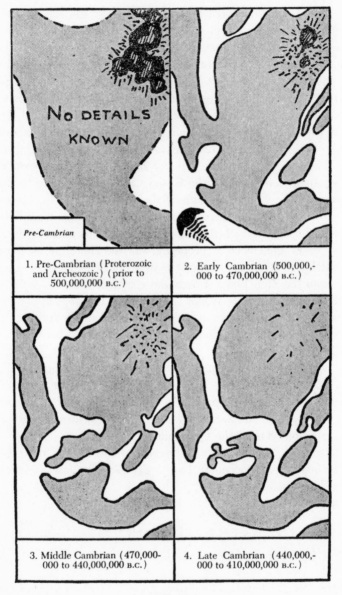

Pre-Cambrian

1. Pre-Cambrian (Proterozoic and Archeozoic) (prior to 500,000,000 B.C.)

2. Early Cambrian (500,000,-000 to 470,000,000 B.C.)

3. Middle Cambrian (470,000-000 to 440,000,000 B.C.)

4. Late Cambrian (440,000,-000 to 410,000,000 B.C.)

Ill. 48

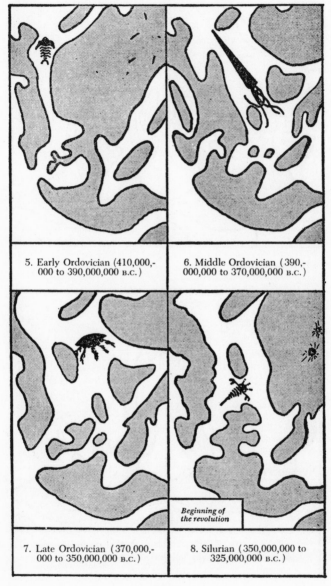

5. Early Ordovician (410,000,-
000 to 390,000,000 B.C.)

6. Middle Ordovician (390,-
000,000 to 370,000,000 B.C.)

7. Late Ordovician (370,000,-
000 to 350,000,000 B.C.)

8. Silurian (350,000,000 to
325,000,000 B.C.)

*Beginning of
the revolution*

Ill. 49

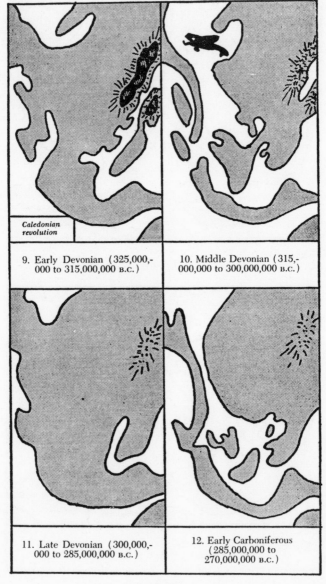

Caledonian
revolution

9. Early Devonian (325,000,-
000 to 315,000,000 B.C.)

10. Middle Devonian (315,-
000,000 to 300,000,000 B.C.)

11. Late Devonian (300,000,-
000 to 285,000,000 B.C.)

12. Early Carboniferous
(285,000,000 to
270,000,000 B.C.)

Ill. 50

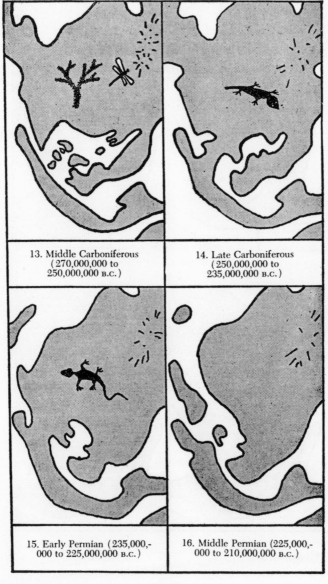

13. Middle Carboniferous
(270,000,000 to
250,000,000 B.C.)

14. Late Carboniferous
(250,000,000 to
235,000,000 B.C.)

15. Early Permian (235,000,-
000 to 225,000,000 B.C.)

16. Middle Permian (225,000,-
000 to 210,000,000 B.C.)

Ill. 51

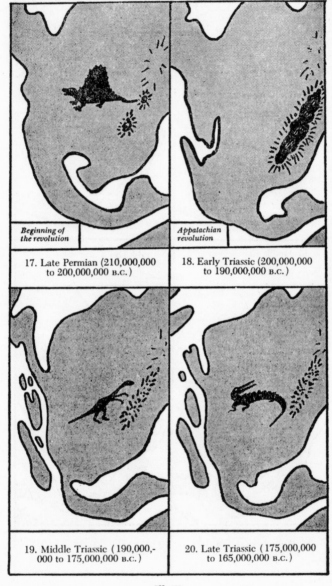

Beginning of
the revolution

Appalachian
revolution

17. Late Permian (210,000,000
to 200,000,000 B.C.)

18. Early Triassic (200,000,000
to 190,000,000 B.C.)

19. Middle Triassic (190,000,-
000 to 175,000,000 B.C.)

20. Late Triassic (175,000,000
to 165,000,000 B.C.)

Ill. 52

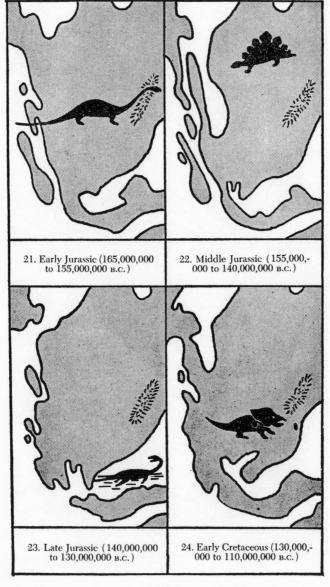

21. Early Jurassic (165,000,000 to 155,000,000 B.C.)

22. Middle Jurassic (155,000,-000 to 140,000,000 B.C.)

23. Late Jurassic (140,000,000 to 130,000,000 B.C.)

24. Early Cretaceous (130,000,-000 to 110,000,000 B.C.)

Ill. 53

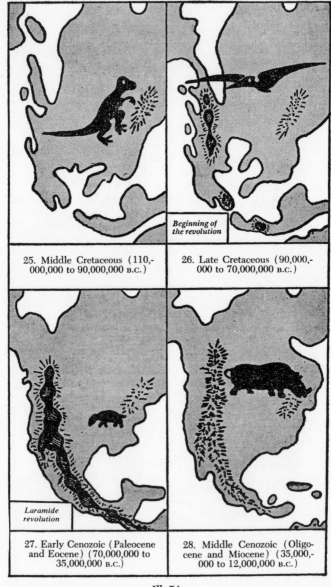

25. Middle Cretaceous (110,-000,000 to 90,000,000 B.C.)

26. Late Cretaceous (90,000,-000 to 70,000,000 B.C.)

Beginning of the revolution

27. Early Cenozoic (Paleocene and Eocene) (70,000,000 to 35,000,000 B.C.)

28. Middle Cenozoic (Oligocene and Miocene) (35,000,-000 to 12,000,000 B.C.)

Laramide revolution

Ill. 54

29. Late Cenozoic (Pliocene) (12,000,000 to 1,000,000 B.C.)

30. Early Quaternary (Pleistocene) (1,000,000 to 10,000 B.C.)

31. Late Quaternary (Recent) (10,000 B.C. to the present)

32. The Future

Ill. 55

general features of the revolutionary epochs and the intervening periods of slow decay and submergence that permit the division of the "book" into well-defined chapters. We have mentioned, however, that changes on a smaller scale were going on all the time, causing permanent alterations in the surface of our planet. In order to represent all these changes continuously, we should have to draw separate maps for each hundred years at least, and then run them through a motion-picture projector. Aside from the fact that present geologic knowledge is far from complete enough to make such an undertaking possible, a film in which each frame represents a century of the Earth's history would run continuously, day and night, for more than two weeks (at the standard film speed of 16 frames per second).

We are therefore reducing this project to a more modest scale, giving thirty-two separate maps (Illus. 48-55) representing the state of the continent of North America over a period of 500,000,-000 years. These are adapted from the paleogeographic maps of Charles Schuchert, published in *Historical Geology* by Charles Schuchert and Carl O. Dunbar.

PALEONTOLOGICAL CURIOSITIES

It is appropriate that this chapter should close with an example of a solution to one of the mysteries which geologists and paleontologists encounter often in their work. Many solutions which they attain through hard work or lucky accident are more striking than solutions of the "who killed cock robin" kind of mystery in the numerous detective stories which flood the book market today.

In many regions of Wyoming and the neighboring mountain states one finds very peculiar objects. They are pieces of stone, mostly granite, a few inches in diameter, having oval shapes with glossy polished surfaces. Indian craftsmen use them for smoothing the surface of earthenware before putting it into kilns. How did these pieces of granite become so smoothly polished? We know that ocean waves, rolling on beaches and shoveling pieces of gravel about, turn them into smooth oval shapes. But the surface of the pebbles found on the ocean shore is dull and cannot compete in glossiness with the stones found in Wyoming. Besides, this region of the North American continent was never exposed to the ocean's waves.

Generations of geologists have racked their brains over the problem without any success. Then the solution of the mystery came in a quite unexpected way. One of the excavations revealed a skeleton of a dinosaur, a relic of the past which is often found in that part of the country. Between the fossilized ribs of the old beast, exactly where its stomach must have been, was a pile of about a dozen of the glossily polished granite stones.

"Elementary, my dear Watson," Sherlock Holmes would have said. "If you ever lived on a farm, you may recall that chickens usually swallow small pebbles which help to grind the food in their stomachs. Well, dinosaurs apparently had the same habit but, since they were much larger than chickens, they swallowed much larger stones. This glossy surface you see was polished by the muscles of the dinosaur's stomach millions of years ago." And so it was.

6

Weather and Climate

WE LIVE on the bottom of a vast ocean of air which surrounds our globe as a thin transparent veil. One-quarter of the atmosphere is below the level of Santa Fe, New Mexico, which has an elevation of 7000 feet, one-half below the altitude of 16,500 feet, which is just the height of Mount Ararat, and three-quarters of it is below 30,000 feet, which is the height of Mount Everest. But highly rarefied fringes of terrestrial atmosphere extend hundreds of miles above the Earth's surface, and it is difficult to say where our atmosphere becomes merely the very thin gas which fills all interplanetary space. The total weight of terrestrial atmosphere is 5,000,000,000,000,000 tons, which, although a large number in itself, is nevertheless only one-third of one per cent of the total weight of water in the oceans. Atmospheric air is composed of 75.5 per cent nitrogen, 23.1 per cent oxygen, 0.9 per cent the inert gas argon, 0.03 per cent carbon dioxide, and negligible amounts of some other gases. Up to the height of about 6 miles, air contains varying amounts of water vapor which originates from evaporation of moisture from the ocean and land surfaces and is carried upward by ascending convective currents. When the warm air rises it expands and becomes cooler, which accounts for the steady decrease in temperature with increasing height. At the altitude of 1½ miles, air temperature drops to the freezing point of water, and it continues to decrease steadily, dropping to about $-100°$ F. at the altitude of 6 miles. The vertical convective currents do not penetrate beyond that height, and at greater altitudes air remains free of humidity and at a constant temperature. The part of the terrestrial atmosphere extending up to the height of 6 miles is known as the *troposphere,* and the physical phenomena occurring in it are of paramount importance for life on the Earth's surface. Storms, hurricanes, tornadoes, and typhoons originate here; all kinds of clouds are formed, to shower rain, snow, and hail on our heads. Beyond the upper limits of the troposphere conditions are much quieter and the sky is always blue. This is the *stratosphere,* through which pilots of airliners like to fly. The change of temperature with increasing altitude in the atmosphere is shown in Illus. 56.

With the exception of the chemically inert gas argon, all components of air play an important role in supporting life on the Earth. Proteins, which form the major part of all living organisms, are composed essentially of carbon, hydrogen, oxygen, and nitrogen. Growing plants get their carbon by absorbing and decomposing atmospheric carbon dioxide under the action of sunlight. Carbon is used to build sugars and other organic material, while oxygen is liberated back into the atmosphere. Hydrogen and oxygen in the form of water are brought in through the roots from the soil, where water gathers from rainfall. Atmospheric nitrogen is assimilated by certain bacteria in the soil, and turned into a variety of fertilizing material necessary for the growth of plants. Thus it is only fair that, when we speak about "Mother Earth," we do not forget "Father Air."

Plants and animals living on the surface of the Earth exert, on their side, a considerable influence on the composition of the atmosphere. It has been estimated that plants consume yearly 500 billion tons of carbon dioxide, transforming it into organic materials. This figure is about one-third of the total carbon-dioxide content of the atmosphere, and if the supply were not constantly replenished it would run out in three short years. It may be mentioned here that only one-tenth of the total carbon-dioxide consumption is due to grass, bushes, and trees, the other nine-tenths being accounted for by algae in the oceans. The con-

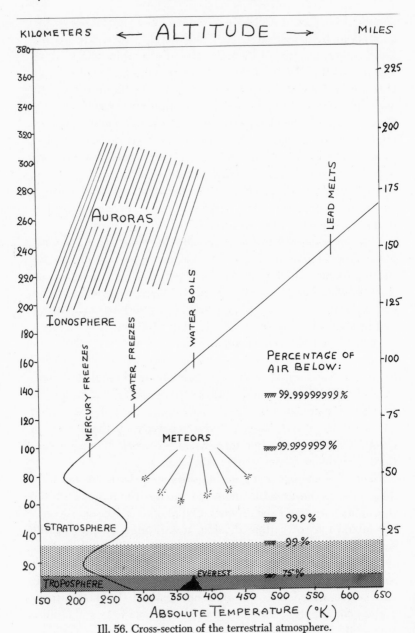

Ill. 56. Cross-section of the terrestrial atmosphere.

sumption of atmospheric carbon dioxide is compensated for by its formation in the processes of animal and plant respiration (plants consume oxygen at night), by the rotting of dead plants and fallen leaves, and by occasional forest fires; therefore it maintains a steady balance through the millennia.

If there were no organic life on the Earth, atmospheric oxygen would gradually disappear as a result of various inorganic oxidation processes, being transformed mostly into carbon dioxide. Such a situation seems to exist on Venus, whose atmosphere, according to spectroscopic studies, contains very large amounts of carbon dioxide and no detectable trace of free oxygen. This fact represents a strong indication that there is no life on the surface of that planet.

Another important function of terrestrial atmosphere is that it turns the Earth into a giant greenhouse, keeping it at a mean temperature of about 60° F., higher than it would be otherwise. The functioning of greenhouses, in which such plants as orchids and strawberries are grown, is based on the fact that glass, being almost completely transparent to visible light, which brings most of the Sun's energy, is opaque to the heat rays which are emitted by the object warmed up by the Sun's radiation. Thus, solar energy entering through the glass roof of a greenhouse is trapped inside and maintains a temperature well above the outside temperature. In the case of our atmosphere the role of glass is played by carbon dioxide and water vapor, which, even though present in minor amounts, absorb very strongly heat rays emitted from the Earth's warm surface and radiate them back to the Earth. Thus the excess heat which is removed from the Earth's surface during the daytime by the convective air currents is resupplied during the cold nights. The moderating effect of the atmosphere can best be demonstrated by comparing the Earth with the Moon, which gets exactly the same amount of heat but has no atmosphere. Measurements of the Moon's surface temperature, carried out by special heat-sensitive instruments known as *bolometers*, show that on the illuminated side of the Moon the temperature of the rocks rises to 214° F., while it drops to −243° F. on the Moon's dark side. Thus if our Earth had no atmosphere water would boil during the daytime, and alcohol would freeze during the night!

While controlling the visible sunlight to keep the Earth's surface warm and comfortable, our atmosphere protects us from various much less pleasant kinds of radiation from the Sun. Apart from visible light, our Sun is known to emit rather large quantities of ultraviolet radiation, X rays, and high-energy particles, which would have a deadly effect on plant and animal life if permitted to penetrate all the way to the surface. But all these dangerous rays are absorbed in the upper layers of the atmosphere, and only a negligible fraction of ultraviolet comes through in just the proper amount to tan the bodies of vacationers on the beaches.

Last but not least, is the mechanical protection our atmosphere gives us against constant bombardment by meteorites of various sizes (with the exception of the biggest ones, which come rarely), and against artificial satellites and the rockets used to put them into orbit, which completely burn and disintegrate after their re-entry into the air.

EARTH'S ENERGY BALANCE

Practically everything that happens on the Earth's surface (except earthquakes and volcanic eruptions) depends on the energy supplied by the sun's radiation. The amount of solar radiation falling on a square-inch area at the distance of the Earth from the Sun outside of the terrestrial atmosphere represents the power of about 1 watt and is hardly sufficient to operate a small flashlight bulb. But if we multiply that figure by the geometric cross-section of the Earth we get, for the total power coming from the Sun to the Earth, a figure of 170 billion megawatts.*
About 40 per cent of all incident energy is reflected and partially absorbed by the clouds which normally cover about half of the

---

* A megawatt is equal to 1 million watts. An average electric bulb uses 60 watts.

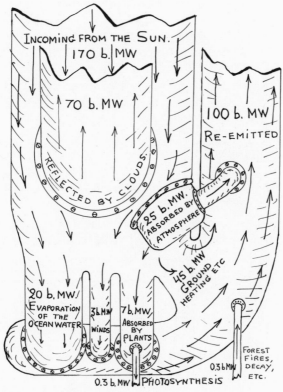

Ill. 57. Heat-balance of the Earth.

Earth's surface, and about 15 per cent is absorbed in the atmosphere before reaching the surface. Thus, only about 45 per cent of the total incident solar energy, i.e., about 75 billion megawatts, reaches and is absorbed by the land and ocean areas. About one-quarter of all that incoming power, or 20 billion megawatts, is spent daily on the evaporation of one thousand billion tons of water, mostly from the ocean surface. Water vapor carried by winds condenses later in the clouds and pours refreshing rains on the thirsty continental areas. About 2 billion megawatts are spent on the maintenance of winds and of ocean currents, which transport some 15 per cent of all incoming heat from the tropical to

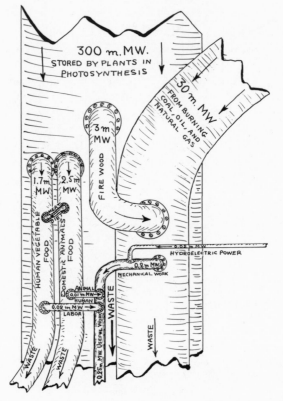

Ill. 58. Heat-balance of life processes.

the polar regions. About 7 billion megawatts are absorbed by plants, and only less than half of one per cent of that amount, or 0.3 billion megawatts, is used in the process of photosynthesis. The rest of the incoming energy is reradiated back into space, either from the Earth's surface or from the atmosphere. If we schematize this distribution of incoming solar energy by drawing a system of branching pipes with cross-sections proportional to the power flux, we obtain the picture shown in Illus. 57.

We can now follow the distribution of power that goes into the production of organic material in plants shown by the pipe system in Illus. 58. Most of it goes to waste. Only 2 per cent of synthesized plant material is used by the population of the Earth as vegetable food, and another 1.5 per cent is used to feed domestic animals. One more per cent is used as firewood, both for home heating and cooking and for industrial purposes. A tiny connection running from the animal-food pipe to the human-food pipe represents the meat diet of humanity; the rest of the food is vegetables and fish. The firewood pipe, carrying about 3 million megawatts, empties into a much broader pipe which carries 30 million megawatts of heat obtained by burning coal, oil, and natural gas. These irreplaceable sources were made available to us by photosynthetic activity of the plants which grew during long-past geological eras.

Now we come to the conversion of heat into mechanical work, where we sustain terrific losses. The combined flow of coal, oil, natural-gas, and firewood heat gives rise to only 200,000 megawatts of mechanical energy. To this are added 20,000 megawatts of manual work by human laborers, and 10,000 megawatts of work done by draft animals. A tiny pipe leading directly from the main source of solar energy and carrying the power of 20,000 megawatts represents the power supplied by hydroelectric installations.

WORLD WINDS

The amount of heat from the Sun that falls on different parts of the Earth's surface depends on their geographical locations. Equatorial regions, where at noon the Sun is almost directly overhead, receive the maximum amount of heat. Polar regions, where the Sun hardly rises above the horizon, receive very little heat. As all readers will remember from their schooldays, this situation is somewhat complicated by the fact that the Earth's rotation axis is not perpendicular to the plane of its orbit around the Sun but is inclined by 23.5 angular degrees. Since the Earth's rotation axis always maintains the same direction in space while the Earth follows its annual path around the Sun, one half-year the northern hemisphere and another half-year the southern hemisphere are turned toward the Sun and consequently get more heat during that period. This periodic change in the amount of heat falling on the two hemispheres accounts for the seasonal changes, the northern winter coinciding with the southern summer, and vice versa. The cold air from the polar regions moves toward the equator, replacing the warm air, and thus causing the general circulation of the atmosphere. If the Earth were not rotating around its axis, atmospheric circulation would be quite simple. Air heated by the Sun's rays in equatorial regions would rise upward, being replaced by cold air flowing along the Earth's surface from the polar regions. This rising warm air would cool off and flow at high altitudes northward and southward to replace the cold air flowing at low altitudes toward the equator. If that were the case, the entire northern hemisphere would experience steady cold northerly wind, with the opposite situation occuring in the southern hemisphere. But, due to the rotation of the Earth, cold air masses traveling from poles to equator and warm air masses traveling from the equator to the poles are deflected from their straight meridional motion. It is easy to understand the reason for that deflection. Since our Earth rotates as a solid sphere, the velocities with which the points on its surface are carried around decreases with the increasing latitude. At the equator that velocity is about 1000 miles per hour; at the latitude of New York, only 900 miles per hour; at Alaska and Hudson Bay, 800 miles per hour; at Spitsbergen, only 640 miles per hour; and at the poles, of course, zero. Since cold air masses traveling along the Earth's surface from polar to equatorial regions must retain their initial velocities according to the basic law of inertia, the ground across which they travel will, so to speak, run ahead of them. As seen by the ground observer, cold winds from the north will be deflected westward. Such winds blowing in northeast-to-southwest directions are known as *easterlies*. In the same way, air masses traveling from equatorial regions to the poles will enter the latitudes at which the velocity of the ground is less than the original velocity of the air masses. As a result, the air masses will have higher velocities than the ground over which they move, and the streams of air will be deflected eastward. In

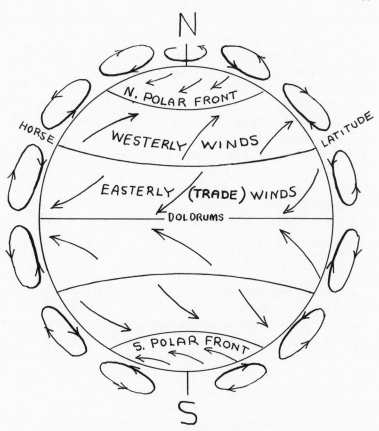

Ill. 59. General circulation of the atmosphere.

this case we will observe winds blowing from southwest to north-east, which are known as *westerlies.*

Because of that sideways sliding of air masses moving from poles to equator and back, the two giant whirlpools that would exist in the northern and southern hemispheres, if the Earth were not rotating, break up into a number of smaller circulation systems connected among themselves as are cogwheels in a gear box (Illus. 59). There are three such separate circulation systems in each of the two hemispheres, as follows.

1. The *polar zone,* extending from each pole to about 60 degrees northern or southern latitude. Here the cold air moves essentially from east to west, forming two giant freezing whirlpools which characterize the Arctic and Antarctic regions.

2. The *temperate zone,* between the 60th and 30th northern or southern latitudes (Hudson Bay to Florida in North America), with prevailing westerly winds.

3. The *subtropical zone,* forming a belt 60 degrees wide around the equator, where warm winds blow mostly from east to west. Those are the so-called "trade winds," which were so helpful to the Spanish and Portuguese explorers of Central and South America.

While within each zone the winds are rather steady and strong, the boundaries between the zones, where the air moves mostly upward or downward, are characterized by almost windless conditions. The boundaries between temperate and subtropical air-circulation zones are known as the *horse latitudes,* a name which is believed to have originated at the time when horses were transported by sailing ships from Europe to America. When the ship was delayed in its sailing across the ocean by a long-extended calm, the horses had to be thrown overboard, since there was not enough hay to feed them, and the bottom of the North Atlantic along the 30th parallel is said to be covered by innumerable horse skeletons. Similarly no good sailing winds blow along the equator, in the belt known to seamen as the *doldrums.*

The boundaries between the polar winds and the prevailing westerlies of the temperate zones are known as *the polar fronts,* and are very important for weather conditions in the temperate zones (Illus. 60, at top). These boundaries are essentially unstable, and there is a constant fight between the cold air advancing from the polar regions and the warm and moist air coming up from lower latitudes. Since cold air is heavier than warm air, the collision between two onrushing air masses forces the warm air to climb on top of the cold air as if the latter were a mountain range. Being lifted up, the warm, moist air cools, and its moisture is liberated, forming thick layers of heavy clouds. Rain, snow, and strong winds always accompany the advance

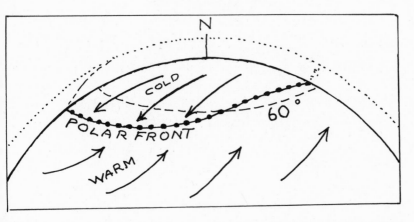

SOUTH   NORTH

Ill. 60. *Above:* The advance of the polar front. *Below:* A conflict between
cold and warm air.

or retreat of the polar front, making the inhabitants of the involved location just as miserable as city inhabitants caught between two battle lines. Depending on the relative strengths of
the polar winds and the westerlies, the polar front swings northward and southward in a rather unpredictable way, shifting sometimes by as much as 1000 miles in a single day. In general the
northern polar front recedes toward the pole (as far as Hudson
Bay) during the summer months, and advances southward (as
far as Florida) during the winter months, causing the fruit
growers to tremble for their citrus groves (Illus. 60, bottom).

Ill. 61. Circulation in world oceans, according to W. Munk. The arrows added in the Arctic Ocean represent recent Russian studies of the icefield drift.

WINDS AND OCEAN CURRENTS

The world pattern of the winds blowing over the surface of the oceans, which cover about 70 per cent of the Earth's surface, is reflected in the motion of the water masses known as ocean currents. But, while the general circulation of the atmosphere is largely unrestricted by the surface features of our globe, the circulation of the ocean waters is strongly limited by continents separating various large water basins. The system of currents in the oceans of the world is shown in Illus. 61, which is drawn

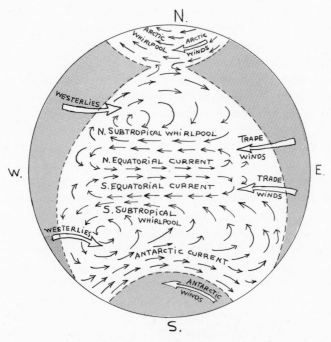

Ill. 62. The schematic relation between prevailing winds and ocean currents (for either the Atlantic or Pacific Ocean).

in a rather unusual cartographic projection, especially designed to show all the important oceans in one piece.

At first sight it seems that the pattern of ocean currents is so complicated that it is impossible to explain it in a simple way. However, a more detailed study of the problem shows a definite correlation between the patterns of the atmospheric and the oceanic movements. A highly simplified model of an ocean basin, be it the Pacific or the Atlantic, is shown in Illus. 62. The shaded areas on the right and on the left represent the continental barriers (North and South America and Eurasia plus Africa, or vice versa) limiting the major ocean basins. In the north we have the Arctic Ocean, which is contrasted with the Antarctic continent in the south. The major winds are shown by large white arrows. The black arrows indicate the directions of ocean currents which could be expected as the result of these winds. The trade winds, blowing westward on both sides of the equator, result in north and south equatorial currents, which move in the same direction. These two currents are compensated by an opposite current flowing through the quiet doldrums region. The combination of the easterlies (trade winds), at the lower latitudes, and the westerlies, at the higher latitudes, produces two subtropical whirlpools which rotate clockwise in the Northern Hemisphere and counterclockwise in the Southern. However, this symmetry between the Northern and Southern Hemispheres is broken up in the polar regions. The waters of the Arctic Ocean, being driven by easterly polar winds, form the arctic whirlpool, moving in an east-to-west direction. The situation on the opposite end of the globe is entirely different, due to the fact that instead of the open Arctic Ocean we have here a large Antarctic continent of about the same size. Thus, the Antarctic winds become inoperative in affecting the motion of waters, and the prevailing role is played by westerlies, which make the water surrounding the Antarctic continent move in a west-to-east direction. Comparing this very simplified theoretical picture with the actual ocean-current pattern as given in Illus. 61, we find general similarity, in spite of the fact that the simplified pattern is badly distorted by the irregularities of the continental shorelines.

ATMOSPHERIC WHIRLPOOLS

The constant battle between the cold northern polar air pushing southward and the warm air masses trying to push it back causes the front line to bend and twist, and situations often develop which the military could call "fluid," where the two rival lines get entangled in a death grip. As shown in Illus. 63, cold air masses may try to execute an "envelopment movement" on the left side of some battle sector and to come to the rear of the opposing warm air masses. What happens in this case is that warm air penetrates the lines of cold air on the eastern section of the front, while cold air achieves a breakthrough on the west-

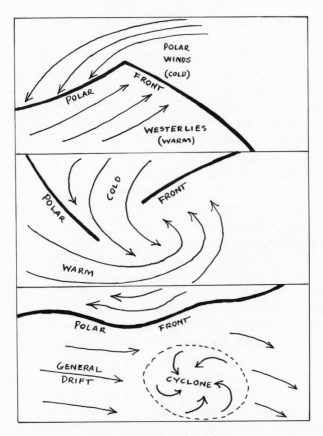

Ill. 63. Formation of a cyclone.

ern section. As a result of that mutual penetration, the opposing air masses start to pirouette wildly (Illus. 63). Since the cold air masses coming south are always deflected westward, while the warm air masses moving north always suffer eastward deflection, the resulting whirlpools, technically known as *cyclones,* always rotate counter-clockwise in the Northern Hemisphere. One can easily see that the same kinds of whirlpools formed at the Antarctic polar front will rotate in the opposite (i.e., clockwise) direction. Newly formed cyclones get detached from the polar fronts (Illus. 63) which gave them their birth and, their original fury being somewhat diminished, move into the temperate zone, driven eastward by westerly winds prevailing at these latitudes. Cyclones move with an average speed of 500 miles per day, and a West Coast cyclone reported on Monday will reach the East Coast by the following weekend.

Thus we see that cyclones represent giant atmospheric air pools in which the air masses spiral toward the center of the disturbance and then soar up almost vertically. Air motion of that kind is always associated with the decrease of the barometric pressure toward the center, since air naturally moves from high-pressure to low-pressure regions. Thus a persistent and rapid fall of the barometer forecasts almost with certainty the approach of a cyclone. Since the air near the ground usually contains a considerable amount of moisture and since it cools rapidly as it rises up in the central region of a cyclone, water vapor condenses into thick clouds which always accompany the passage of a cyclone.

Since in cyclones the ground air moves upward, in the regions between them cold, dry air masses from above must descend toward the ground. Coming down and being compressed, the air becomes pleasantly warm and still drier, and spreads outward from the center. The rotation of the Earth again has the decisive word, and the divergent motion of descending air masses acquires a spiraling character, in this case in a clockwise direction (counter-clockwise in the Southern Hemisphere). These so-called *anticyclones* are much pleasanter than their violent counterparts. The air is warm and dry and the winds rather moderate, and the Sun shines in the blue cloudless sky.

Closely related to cyclones are their more aggressive sisters, tropical hurricanes, or *typhoons* as they are known in the Orient. (We say "sisters" because they are usually called by women's names.) Their origin still presents many riddles to meteorologists, but it is likely that they result from the conflict between the system of winds along the frontiers between the temperate and subtropical zones of air circulation. Since tropical regions receive much more solar heat than polar regions and since the amount of moisture in the air in the tropics is much higher, all the characteristics of these atmospheric whirlpools are strongly amplified. Like cyclones they are associated with the vertical motion of air masses and show counter-clockwise rotation. They are smaller but much more violent than ordinary cyclones; their wind velocities range from 75 to over 150 miles per hour, and they move across the surface of the Earth with a speed of up to 1000 miles per day. Originating mostly over ocean surfaces in the subtropical regions, they move northward (southward in the Southern Hemisphere) and carry peril and destruction to the cities of the temperate zones. Thus we may say that the inhabitants of a temperate zone are being constantly attacked by hostile forces coming either from the north or from the south.

CLOUDS, RAINS, THUNDERSTORMS

As we have already stated, clouds result from the condensation of moisture in air masses which are brought up by vertical air convection currents. Clouds are, in fact, nothing but giant masses of fog consisting of microscopic water droplets floating in the air. Probably the most important, and certainly the most beautiful, are the so-called *cumulus clouds* which tower in the sky during balmy, sunny summer days. They are the result of the condensation of water vapor produced by the heat of the Sun's rays at the surface of continents and oceans, and usually occur in the quiet areas of anticyclones. Under certain conditions of air circulation within the cloud, some of the tiny water droplets grow bigger and bigger at the expense of other droplets, which grow smaller and disappear. The growing droplets finally become so large and heavy that the friction of the air cannot support them any longer, and they begin to descend through the cloud, capturing more moisture and becoming still bigger. When this happens, a refreshing summer shower pours down on our heads.

Another "peaceful" breed is the so-called *cirrus cloud* (*cirrus* means "feather" in Latin), which floats at much higher altitudes than those of cumulus clouds. The air at these high altitudes is very cold and, instead of small water droplets, cirruses are composed of microscopic crystals of ice. When during the night a cirrus cloud comes in front of the Moon, the reflection of moonlight from the icicles produces beautiful rings or haloes around the Moon's face.

A sharp contrast to the peaceful and beautiful cumuluses and cirruses is presented by cloud formations which result from more violent forms of activity such as take place along the polar fronts, in cyclones, and in hurricanes. Here, owing to the violence of air motion, large masses of moist air are lifted rapidly to high altitudes and the condensation of water vapor proceeds on an unprecedented scale. It results in the formation of heavy, dense clouds, known as *nimbuses,* extending over large areas of the Earth's surface. Since at these altitudes the temperature is well below the freezing point of water, the vapor condenses into small ice crystals which, falling down through the cloud, grow in size by the accretion of more and more water vapor. If the air between the base of the cloud and the surface of the Earth is warm, as it is during the summer, these ice crystals may melt again, resulting in heavy and persistent rainfall. During the winter, however, they come down unmelted in the form of snow.

Violent dynamical activity in the perturbed regions of the troposphere results in equally violent electric disturbances, producing the electric tension of many millions of volts between different parts of a single cloud, between neighboring clouds, and between the clouds and the ground below them. As a result, lightning shines and thunder roars. In olden times it was believed that lightning and thunder were caused by the divine blacksmith, Thor, striking his hammer against his heavenly anvil. We do not believe this now, but we must confess that we cannot account for them much better than ancient mythology did. A trickle of truth may come from the half-century-old discovery of the British physicist C.T.R. Wilson, who proved that water vapor condenses more readily on air particles carrying a negative electric charge than on those carrying a positive charge. Thus, the negative electric charge will be brought down by rain particles into the lower part of the cloud, while the positive charge will be left in the upper part of it. This will produce a sufficiently high difference in the electric potential for lightning to strike between the clouds, and between the clouds and the ground. But all these phenomena are so complicated that there are just as many different opinions about them as there are scientists studying them.

WEATHER PREDICTION AND CONTROL

That weather forecasting is notoriously uncertain is indicated in the well-known English rhyme:

> *Whether it's cold, or whether it's hot,*
> *We shall have weather, whether or not;*

and in the less well-known Russian verse by Demian Biedny. In this verse there is a passage about a barometer which hung in a shop window and was advertised as "A great bargain! A barometer — an instrument that tells the weather!" Biedny continues:

> *Some simpleton thought it a wonderful buy,*
> *And after he'd bought it (believing the lie)*
> *He grinned at the salesman. "Now tell me," he said,*
> *"Which end shows the weather — the tail or the head?"*
>
> *"Up to you.*
> *Both'll do.*
> *Put it out of the window and count up to ten,*
> *Hold it there a bit longer and check it again;*
> *It'll mean if you find the barometer dry*
> *That there isn't a cloud to be seen in the sky.*
> *If it's wet, that means rain."*
>
> *Said the fool, raising Cain,*
> *"Some contraption you've saddled me with! It's no good!*
> *I could tell all that stuff by myself, yes I could!"*
>
> *"That is plain,"*
> *Said the salesman, enjoying this more than he should,*
> *"So you could."* ...

---

*Rendered into English by B.P.G.

However, modern meteorology does a reasonably good job of the art of weather prediction. Information on barometric pressure, temperature, humidity, wind direction and strength, etc., is broadcast to central meteorological offices from a large number of stations scattered all over the world. On the basis of these data, meteorologists construct so-called synoptical maps which show day-to-day changes in the weather pattern and permit them to predict, with some degree of reliability, the weather conditions to be expected in the near future. Two such maps pertaining to the change of meteorological pattern within 24 hours might show that a high-pressure region (anticyclone) centered in Utah one day had moved to northern Arizona the next day, while a low-pressure area (cyclone) centered in southeastern Kansas had shifted to eastern Pennsylvania. Watching these changes, experienced weather forecasters can predict with some assurance how the synoptic pattern will look tomorrow, the day after tomorrow, or even a week ahead. Knowing the kind of weather prevailing in different parts of cyclones and anticyclones, they can make guesses whether "next weekend" will be fine for picnicking or whether a storm warning should be given to the fishermen at Cape Hatteras.

But although the prediction turns out to be more or less true in many cases, this method of weather forecasting still remains an art rather than a science. Considerable conversation but comparatively little action is now current in relation to giving the work of weather forecasting to high-speed electronic computers, which should be able to solve the complex hydrodynamical problem of the motion of air masses on the basis of observed data on the Earth's surface and those obtained by balloons or rocket flights at different altitudes, or more recently by weather satellites. Solving the problem is admittedly difficult but certainly worth the effort.

Once this is done, meteorologists will also be able to tackle the problem of controlling the weather, at least within certain limits. It is possible that comparatively small changes of surface conditions could result in essential changes of the weather pattern. A few hundred bombers loaded with coal dust, scattering it all over the glaciers of Greenland, may increase the absorption of solar radiation in that region, which can influence the motion of the cold air masses coming from the polar front. It has also been suggested by Stanislav Ulam of the Los Alamos Scientific Laboratory that a small atomic bomb detonated near the eye of a tropical hurricane can deflect it from its original path and save a lot of human life and property in the Atlantic Coast states.

But the possible effects of human influence on the weather cannot be evaluated until we know how to use fast electronic computers for accurate prediction of weather in general.

THE HISTORY OF CLIMATE

Climate is a mysterious word. Professional climatologists would define it as a listing of minimum and maximum temperatures for every month of the year, of absolute and relative humidity, of the number of sunny days, of the percentage of sky covered on non-sunny days, of the average precipitation for each month, etc. But even if one knows all these figures, it would be difficult to decide whether the climate is good or bad, or worth talking about at all.

If, however, we use this dry scientific definition of climate, we find that climate in different localities changes quite noticeably before our eyes. For example, one finds that within the last thirty years the climate of eastern North America and northern Europe has become slightly warmer. An extreme case of climatic change is presented by Spitsbergen, where the average temperature during the month of January increased by about 5° F. between 1913 and 1937. It seems that, in the course of the present century, the climate of the Northern Hemisphere has become warmer and the glaciers descending from the mountaintops are gradually retreating. There is evidence that the polar caps, which at present cover about 3 per cent of the Earth's surface, melt at the rate of 2 feet per year (i.e., the surface of the ice comes down that fast). The water resulting from the melting of the ice, being distributed all over the oceans, raises the ocean level by about 1 inch per

Ill. 64. The "ice river" of a glacier descending a mountain slope.
(*Courtesy of the U.S. Geologic Survey*)

year or 10 feet per century. If the polar caps were to be completely melted, the ocean level would rise by 200 feet, thus flooding all major coastal cities. But this would require the total energy supplied by the Sun to the Earth in the course of 2½ years, and, since only a negligible fraction of that energy is absorbed by snow and ice in the polar regions, hundreds of thousands of years may pass before that happens.

While all the climatic changes observed by us directly pertain to the time periods which are nothing but a wink as compared with the geological history of our globe, geological evidence indicates that much larger changes took place during the hundreds of thousands and millions of years past. Only about 25,000 years ago, giant glaciers descending from the northern highlands covered with thick layers of ice the lowlands further south, which are today comfortable regions for human habitation. In America these ice sheets covered about half of the present area of the

United States, extending as far south as New York, Kansas City, and San Francisco. In Europe, the present sites of London, Berlin, and Moscow were hidden under thick layers of ice. Moving down the mountain slopes, ice masses tore off large boulders and carried them along, either in one piece or ground up into fine gravel and sand. Giant boulders perched in perilous positions in the vicinity of New York City (Illus. 65) and many other American and European cities give undeniable proof that, not too many thousands of years ago, glaciers which brought them along had extended that far south.

The sand and the thin stone dust (silt) which resulted from the grinding of the rocks were carried along and deposited at the edge of the advancing ice sheets. When, later on, the ice retreated, this granulated material was carried south by winds and spread over large areas of flat lands. The deserts in North America and the sands of the Sahara are most probably of that origin. Moving southward, the sheets of ice also dug deep grooves whenever they passed over comparatively soft surface material.

Ill. 65. A large stone, once carried by a glacier, now resting on the rocky ground polished by ice during the last glacial period. (Not far from New York City!)   *(Courtesy of the U.S. Geologic Survey)*

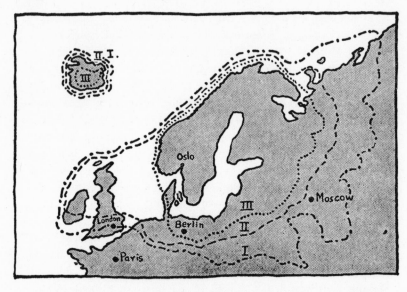

Ill. 66. Maximum extension of the last three glacial sheets over Europe.

The Great Lakes in North America, and many lake regions in northern Europe, owe their origin to the work of moving glaciers.

If we go further back in geological history, the situation turns out to be entirely different. Studying the deposits formed about 40,000 years ago, we find that the climate was much warmer. In the deposits formed in northern Europe are numerous fossils of palms and other plants which cannot possibly grow today at these latitudes. In America the fossilized leaves of magnolia are found as far north as the states of Oregon and Washington. Oaks, chestnut trees, and maples grew in Alaska, Greenland, and Spitsbergen, while the typical boreal plants, such as dwarf birch, flourished at latitudes at which no plants at all can grow today. If, however, we go still further back in time, we find the situation again reversed, and geological evidence indicates that some 60,000 years ago ice sheets spread down the continental plains even farther south than in the most recent glacial advance. In Illus. 66 we show the successive advances and retreats of ice in Europe during the last 600,000 years.

For the earlier geological periods the evidence is considerably more meager, but we find vague indication of possible glaciations during the Appalachian revolution about 150 million years ago. There is also evidence of glaciation in South America, South Africa, India, and Australia at long past eras. But because it was such a long time ago the evidence is not entirely conclusive.

Another method of studying paleotemperatures (the temperatures of the past) was proposed recently by the famous American scientist Harold Urey. In Chapter 5 we mentioned that limestone deposits on the bottoms of the ancient seas are formed by the "skeletons" of the tiny marine animals which lived at that time. Chemically the limestone is *calcium carbonate* ($CaCO_3$), which was originally dissolved in the sea water. Modern nuclear physics shows that the element oxygen (O) consists of two kinds of atoms known as isotopes, having different weights but identical chemical properties. The lighter isotope (O^{16}) forms 99.8 per cent of the entire amount, while the heavier isotope (O^{18}) forms only 0.2 per cent. When calcium carbonate is formed by a chemical reaction in the ocean waters, the relative percentages of the two oxygen isotopes (O^{16} and O^{18}) incorporated into the $CaCO_3$ molecule depends on the water temperature. This calcium carbonate, originally dissolved in the ocean water, is absorbed by microscopic marine animals and incorporated into their calcareous shells. After the animals' death, the shells descend to the bottom and form limestone deposits. Thus, said Urey, by studying the relative amounts of O^{16} and O^{18} isotopes in different limestone deposits, it should be possible to tell what the ocean temperature was when these deposits were formed. Boring into the ocean bottom, in comparatively shallow places, one could extract samples of limestone formed at different eras, and, by measuring the oxygen-isotope ratios, the temperature during these eras could be determined. Illus. 67*a* represents the results of such an analysis for the past 100,000 years. Ocean temperatures obtained by Cesare Emiliani for three different samples of sedimentary layers at the ocean's bottom are plotted against the age of these deposits. The chronology of these deposits was determined by Hans Suess on the basis of the rates of sedimentation

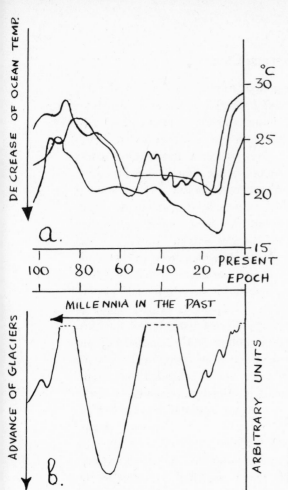

Ill. 67. Variation of ocean temperatures (*a*) and the advances of glaciers (*b*) during the last 100,000 years.

indicated by radioactive-carbon measurements of the three cores for the first 30,000 years.* The resulting variations of the ocean's temperature stands in reasonable agreement with the lower curve (*b*), representing the advances and retreats of the European glaciers obtained by conventional geological methods.

* The radioactive carbon isotope C^{14} is produced in the atmosphere from ordinary nitrogen (N^{14}) by the impact of high-energy cosmic rays, and is incorporated into plant tissues (algae in the ocean) by the process of photosynthesis. It decays with a half-life of 5700 years, changing back into N^{14}. The American chemist Willard Libby developed a method of estimating the age of old organic deposits by measuring the amount of C^{14} still contained in them.

WHAT CAUSED PERIODIC "COLD WAVES"?

In order to understand the causes of the glaciations that occur periodically on the surface of our globe, we have to remember that we are dealing here with a double periodicity. First of all, *extensive glaciations take place only during the periods of the Earth's history that follow the great revolutions, when the surface of the continents is elevated and covered with high mountains.* This periodicity simply indicates that the existence of such elevations is a prerequisite for the formation of thick sheets of ice, which, growing larger and larger, descend from the mountains and cover extensive areas of the surrounding plains.

But *within each glacial era corresponding to a given revolution there are also periodic changes considerably shorter in duration;* while the mountains are still standing, the ice advances and retreats across the plains many times in succession. This second periodicity is evidently independent of changes in the structural characteristics of the Earth's surface, and must be ascribed to real changes in temperature. Since the heat balance on the surface of the Earth is wholly regulated by the amount of solar radiation falling on it, we must look for possible factors that can affect the amount of incident solar radiation. Factors of this sort may be: 1) variations of the transparency of the terrestrial atmosphere; 2) periodic changes in solar activity; and 3) changes in the Earth's rotation around the Sun.

The purely atmospheric explanation of the variability of climate, which is still favored by many climatologists, rests on the hypothesis that, for one reason or another, the amount of carbon dioxide in our atmosphere is subject to periodic fluctuations with time. Since this constituent of the air is largely responsible for the absorption of heat radiation, a relatively slight decrease in the carbon-dioxide content of the atmosphere might have caused a considerable drop in the surface temperature, resulting in the excessive ice formation characteristic of glacial periods. It must be borne in mind, however, that although such an explanation is in itself quite possible, the reason for these supposed periodic

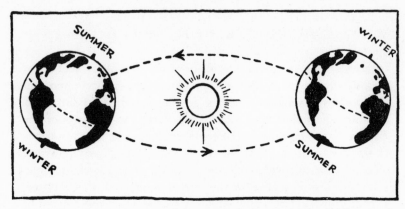

Ill. 68. Familiar explanation of the seasonal changes in the Northern and
Southern Hemispheres.

fluctuations in the composition of the air is not at all clear. Moreover, there is no way of checking whether the extensive glaciations of the past were actually connected with a variation in the
air's carbon-dioxide content.

The hypothesis that seeks to explain the cold spells by variability of solar activity suffers from the same sort of indefiniteness. To
be sure, we do observe periodic changes in solar radiation, caused
by the varying number of sunspots, which reaches a maximum
every 10 or 12 years. It is also true that during the years of sunspot maxima the average terrestrial temperature drops about 2° F.
because of the decrease in the amount of radiation received. But
there are no indications, either observational or theoretical, of
variations of solar activity persisting for thousands of years. Here,
as with the carbon-dioxide hypothesis, it appears to be quite impossible to check the coincidence of past glacial ages with mini-
ma of solar activity.

The last of these three hypotheses is not subject to these stric-
tures, however, and, as we shall see, it not only enables us to
understand the causes of periodic glaciation, but also makes it possible to fix its dates in excellent agreement with geologic evidence.

The reader will remember that the seasonal changes on the
surface of the Earth are due to the fact that its axis of rotation is

inclined to the plane of its orbit, so that for six months the Northern Hemisphere (and another six months the Southern Hemisphere) is turned toward the Sun (Illus. 68). Owing to the longer duration of the day and the more vertical incidence of the solar rays, the hemisphere turned toward the Sun receives considerably more heat and has a summer season, whereas the opposite hemisphere goes through the period of winter cold.

It must be remembered, however, that the Earth's orbit is not exactly a circle, but an ellipse, so that the Earth gets closer to the Sun at some points of its trajectory than at others. At the present time the earth passes through the perihelion of its orbit (i.e., through the point closest to the Sun) at the end of December, and reaches its maximum distance from the Sun at the end of June. *Consequently, winters in the Northern Hemisphere must be somewhat milder than in the Southern, whereas northern summers must be somewhat cooler.* We know from astronomical observation that the distance to the Sun in December is some 3 per cent less than in June, so that the difference in the heat received in opposite hemispheres should amount to 6 per cent, since the intensity of radiation decreases as the inverse square of the distance. Using the relationship between the amount of radiation received and the temperature of the surface,* we find that *at the present time the mean temperature of northern summers must be 7° to 9° F. lower, and the mean temperatures of northern winters 7° to 9° higher, than the corresponding values for the Southern Hemisphere.*

One might think that these differences between the two hemispheres cannot contribute to the explanation of glacial periods, since the colder summers will be compensated for by warmer winters, and vice versa. This is not true, however, because the relative effect of temperature variations upon the formation of ice is quite different for summers and winters. In fact, if the

---

* If L_1 and L_2 represent the amount of heat received, and T_1 and T_2 represent the corresponding surface temperatures in centigrade degrees, we obtain the equation:

$$\frac{T_1 + 273° \text{C.}}{T_2 + 273° \text{C.}} = \sqrt[4]{\frac{L_1}{L_2}}$$

temperature is already below the freezing point (as it usually is during the winter), its further decrease will not influence the amount of snowfall, since all the humidity present in the air is precipitated anyhow. On the other hand, the increase of radiation during the summer will considerably accelerate the melting and removal of the ice formed during the winter months. Thus we must conclude that *colder summers favor the formation of ice sheets much more than colder winters, and that consequently the conditions necessary for extensive glaciation are at present realized in the Northern Hemisphere.*

"But," the reader will probably ask, "why don't we then have glaciation in Europe and North America at the present time, if the climatic conditions favor it?" The answer to this question lies in the absolute value of the temperature difference; and it seems that the cooling of 7° to 9° F. is just below the amount necessary to cause the growth of ice sheets. As we have seen, the glaciers of the Northern Hemisphere are at present retreating rather than advancing. But the balance between the amount of snowfall during the winters and the amount of melted ice during the summers is a very delicate one, and *a drop in summer temperature that is only two or three times larger may completely reverse the situation.*

Looking for the causes of larger temperature differences, which might have caused extensive glaciations of the past, we must turn our attention to possible changes in the direction of the Earth's axis of rotation and in its orbital motion around the Sun. It is well known that the rotation axis of the Earth is slowly changing its position in space, describing a cone whose central line is perpendicular to the plane of the orbit; a phenomenon analogous to that observed in an ordinary spinning top (Illus. 69). This motion of the Earth's axis is known as *precession;* it was explained by Newton as due to the attractive forces of the Sun and the Moon on the Equatorial bulge of the rotating globe. This motion

---

* The name "precession" was introduced in 125 B.C. by Hipparchus, who noticed that the "point of equinox" (i.e., the point on the celestial sphere where the ecliptic crosses the equator) is slowly "preceding" or "stepping forward" to meet the Sun.

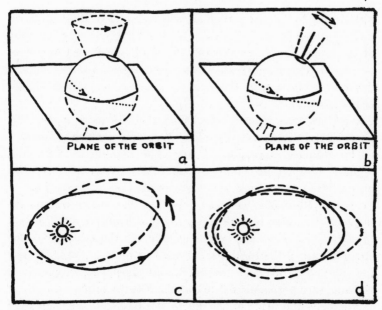

PLANE OF THE ORBIT   *a*

PLANE OF THE ORBIT   *b*

c

d

Ill. 69. Variations of the elements of the Earth's motion: *a*. precession of the axis of rotation; *b*. variation of inclination to the plane of the orbit; *c*. precession of the Earth's orbit; and *d*. changes in the eccentricity of the orbit. (All variations are greatly exaggerated in the diagram.)

of the Earth's axis in space is very slow, taking about 26,000 years to complete the entire cycle. It is clear that the phenomenon of precession will periodically change the situation described on the previous pages, and *that approximately every 13,000 years the Earth will pass through its perihelion with its Northern and Southern Hemispheres alternately turned toward the Sun.* It is also clear that this phenomenon, alternating the climatic differences between the two hemispheres, cannot bring about a more intensive decrease of temperature in either of them; if at present "we could, but do not actually, have an ice age at New York" the same formula will be applicable to Buenos Aires 13,000 years hence.

In addition to ordinary precession, there are other perturbations of the motion of the Earth caused by the action of other planets, by Jupiter, in particular, which, proud of its great mass, tackles almost every little planet of the solar system. The study of these perturbations represents the chief subject of the science of celestial mechanics, which has been brought to the highest degree of precision by the work of many great mathematicians of the past and the present.

We learn from celestial mechanics that the inclination of the Earth's axis of rotation to the plane of its orbit (which is unaffected by ordinary precession) is subject to periodic changes with a period of about 40,000 years (Illus. 69b). Since the very existence of the summer and winter seasons is due to this inclination (compare Illus. 68), we must conclude that *larger inclinations increase the differences between the two hemispheres and lead to warmer summers and colder winters*. On the other hand, the straightening of the Earth's axis leads to a more uniform climate; the differences between seasons would disappear completely if the axis were perpendicular to the plane of the orbit.

Nor does the orbit of the Earth itself remain unchanged; it rotates slowly around the Sun, with periodic increases and decreases in its eccentricity (Illus. 69c and d). Although both changes show a roughly periodic character, the periods vary from 60,000 to 120,000 years, and in order to get an exact picture of these variations one is obliged to use the complicated calculations of celestial mechanics. Fortunately enough, the methods of celestial mechanics are so fabulously precise that *the entire picture of the behavior of the Earth's orbit can be reconstructed as far back as 1 million years with a probable error of not more than 10 per cent*.

The rotation of the orbit around the Sun obviously produces the same effect as the precession of the Earth's axis, and the two phenomena must simply be added together.

Periodic changes of eccentricity are of great importance for climatic conditions in both hemispheres. *During epochs of large elongation of the orbit, the Earth is especially far from the Sun while passing through the most distant point of its trajectory, and the amount of heat received by both hemispheres at that time is exceptionally low*. According to exact calculations, the eccentricity of the Earth's orbit 180,000 years ago, for instance, was 2½ times larger than it is at present, from which it follows that the temperature difference between the Northern and Southern Hemispheres must have been about 16° to 18° F. (see footnote, page 169).

Although the temperature changes resulting from any one of these causes may not be very important, we must remember that if they had all been acting in the same direction at a certain epoch of the Earth's history, the combined effect might have been rather large. Thus, during the epoch when the eccentricity of the orbit was especially large, the inclination of the axis especially small, and the summer season in the Northern Hemisphere occurred while the Earth was passing through the most distant part of its elongated orbit, the amount of heat received in this hemisphere during the summer months must have been exceptionally low.

On the other hand, a smaller eccentricity of the orbit combined with the opposite inclination of the axis of rotation must have caused considerably milder climatic conditions in this hemisphere.

Using the data on the elements of the Earth's motion obtained by the methods of celestial mechanics, a Yugoslav geophysicist, M. Milankovitch, constructed a chart representing climatic variations in the Northern and Southern Hemispheres due to these purely astronomical causes. One of his curves, for the Northern Hemisphere, representing the amount of solar heat received at 65 degrees north latitude during 650,000 past summers, is reproduced in Illus. 70. This curve shows that the unidirectional action of all the three causes mentioned must have taken place in the years 25,000 B.C., 70,000 B.C., 115,000 B.C., 190,000 B.C., 230,000 B.C., 425,000 B.C., 475,000 B.C., 550,000 B.C., and 590,000 B.C. Comparing this theoretical curve with the empirical curve obtained by geologists which represents the maximum extension of the glaciers of the past (as determined by glacial deposits), we find that the agreement is even better than could have been expected. This shows that changes in the earth's orbit and in its axis of rotation must have played an important role in the periods of

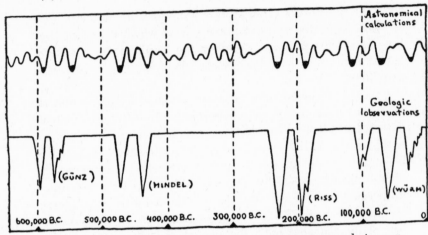

Ill. 70. The upper graph represents the variations of temperature during summers at 65° north latitude (after Milankovitch). The lower graph gives the different glaciation periods as deduced from geological data. The names in parentheses are those of the river valleys in which the deposits formed by various advances of ice were discovered and studied.

glaciation. Similar results were also obtained for the Southern Hemisphere, but in that hemisphere the comparison of theory and observation is much less decisive because of our comparatively meager knowledge concerning glacial advances there.

It is apparent that there must have been a number of separate glacial advances; the geological division of the glacial epochs into only four or five periods is due to the fact that these separate advances have been always associated in close groups of two or three.

In concluding this chapter, we must remind the reader once more that *the periodic succession of warmer and colder climates, caused by purely astronomical factors, must have been taking place at intervals of less than 100,000 years throughout the entire geological history of our planet. It was only during the mountainous stages of the Earth's evolution, however, that conditions were favorable enough for the formation of extensive glaciers by each of these successive cold waves.* Since we are now living more or less in the midst of a mountain-building epoch in the evolution of our planet, with a number of high mountains already standing and a still larger number probably impending, we must expect the ice that retreated some 10,000 years ago to come back again, and that these periodic advances and retreats will continue as long as there are any mountains in northern latitudes. Only when, after many millions of years, all the elevations formed by "our" revolution will have been finally washed away by rains, will glaciers completely disappear from the face of the Earth, the climate become milder and more uniform, and the changes in the Earth's orbit and the inclination of its axis result only in relatively unimportant variations of the average yearly temperatures in different localities. And then, after another hundred or two hundred million years, a new revolution and new periodic glaciations will ensue.

7

Hell above Our Heads

As WAS DISCUSSED in the previous chapter, the lower atmosphere (troposphere), extending to the height of about 6 miles and containing about four-fifths of all air, is in constant interaction with the Earth's surface. It receives heat and moisture by convective currents rising from the ocean surfaces and from the wet ground, and, in its turn, affects life on Earth through winds, clouds, rain, and snow which originate in it.

Beyond the limits of the troposphere begins the so-called *stratosphere*: a quiet layer of dry and transparent air extending to the height of about 50 miles above the Earth's surface. Although the stratosphere is very attractive for air pilots and their passengers, giving them a smooth, pleasant ride, it is of comparatively little interest to scientists because nothing in particular happens there. Too high to be influenced by the Earth's surface, it is not yet high enough to be influenced by the Sun's short-wave radiation, which is absorbed at still higher altitudes.

Only the meteors, usually small particles weighing less than an ounce, penetrate into these quiet air layers. Moving with velocities of 20 miles per second and more, and heated by friction against the air, they melt and burn, leaving long luminous tracks in the sky. Solid products of such burning, in the form of thin dust, float in the stratosphere for months, descending only very slowly into the lower layers of air. Arriving in the troposphere, they join the dust particles brought up from the ground in helping to bring about the condensation of rain droplets. In fact, it has been noticed that strong meteor showers are followed, after a few months' delay, by considerable increase of precipitation all over the Earth's surface.

When the volcano Krakatoa erupted in 1883 with unprecedented force, clouds of fine volcanic dust were thrown high into the stratosphere and remained there for several years before settling down to the ground. Floating at very high altitudes and illuminated by the rays of the Sun, the dust could be seen a long time after sunset, as thin, silvery clouds similar to ordinary cirruses. These particles, being spread all over the stratosphere, reflected between 5 and 10 per cent of the incoming radiation, which lowered the average temperature of the Earth by about 10° F. for a period of several years. Today there are newcomers in the stratosphere — particles of fission products originating in atomic and hydrogen bomb tests. They too float up there for years, descending only very slowly on our heads.

THE IONOSPHERE

Above the height of 50 miles we enter into the region of extremely rarefied air, hundreds of thousands of times rarer than the air near the Earth's surface. This region contains only a small fraction of 1 per cent of the total amount of atmospheric air, but it plays an extremely important role, being the frontier between the atmosphere and outer space. And, as does any frontier, it keeps out hostile invaders. This is the layer of air which stops ultraviolet radiation of the Sun and prevents it from doing fatal damage to life flourishing on the Earth's surface. But as they protect us from incoming ultraviolet radiation, air molecules in the ionosphere themselves suffer a great damage from that source. Atoms, as everybody now knows, consist of nuclei and swarms of electrons revolving around them. While the rays of visible light affect only the motion of electrons within the atom, leaving the basic structure of atoms intact, ultraviolet radiation tears off some of the electrons, catapulting them at high speed through space. Since electrons carry a negative electric charge, atoms which lose one or more electrons become positively charged. We say that the air is *ionized* when it contains positive and negative ions, rather than electrically neutral particles. Because the air at these altitudes is extremely rarefied, collisions between its particles are rather unlikely, and torn-off electrons travel for a long time before they encounter and are captured by some positive ions, thus forming again electrically neutral particles. Because in an ionized gas the positively and negatively charged particles can move freely on their own, the gas becomes a very good conductor of electricity, and strong electric currents flow through it at the slightest provocation.

It is known that good electrical conductors have the properties of reflecting or absorbing electromagnetic waves. Thus, for example, visible light, which is nothing more than short electromagnetic waves, passes without any difficulty through glass (electric insulator) but is partially reflected and partially absorbed by metal surfaces (electric conductors). Similarly, while a radio receiver with a built-in antenna functions quite well inside a frame or stone house, it will not work inside an automobile, where it is surrounded mostly by metal walls.

Therefore the ionosphere surrounding our globe serves as a reflector and partial absorber for radio waves emitted by broadcasting stations. If that were not so, radio communication between the distant points on Earth would be absolutely impossible since the radio waves emitted by the transmitting station would go straight out into space instead of bending around the horizon to reach a distant reception station; indeed, it was a great surprise when in 1901 Marconi established radio communications between Europe and America. As it happens, however, radio waves find themselves locked between two electrically conductive layers, the Earth's surface and the ionosphere, and, through a series of successive reflections, propagate far and wide along the curved surface of our globe.

A few words may be said about temperatures prevailing in the ionosphere. As we discussed earlier, the temperature in the troposphere drops steadily down to about $-100°$ F. at the altitude of 6 miles and remains close to that value all through the stratosphere up to an altitude of about 50 miles. But, if we go still higher, air temperature begins to rise. At an elevation of 80 miles it reaches normal room temperature; at 100 miles it equals the temperature of boiling water, and at 150 miles it is the temperature of molten lead. The reason for that rapid temperature increase at high altitudes is ultraviolet radiation from the Sun.

When electrons are torn off from the air molecules by ultra-violet rays, both the electrons and the resulting positive ions acquire very high velocities, which, according to the kinetic theory of heat, means very high temperature. One should not think, however, that in these high altitudes one would be roasted alive. Although the air molecules there have the velocity they would have at these high temperatures near the Earth's surface, the density of the air is so extremely low that its ability to transfer heat becomes practically negligible. In a warm or a cool room on the ground, each square inch of our skin receives about 10^{27} (1 followed by 27 zeros!) molecular impacts per second, and this enormous number of impacts heats our bodies very quickly. At the altitude of 150 miles, this number of collisions is reduced by a factor of many billions, and the inflow of heat by conduction becomes correspondingly slower. Thus, in spite of the fact that the temperature of the air at that altitude equals the melting temperature of lead, a man would freeze to death there, simply because the amount of heat lost by his body through thermal radiation would be much larger than the amount of heat supplied by the conductivity of the air.

PARTICLES FROM THE SUN

"Even the Sun has spots," goes the proverb, suggesting that, apart from the spots, the solar surface is calm and smooth. Nothing could be farther from the truth. Photographs taken through large telescopes, and more recently by cameras flown in rockets into the upper layers of the atmosphere, show that the surface of

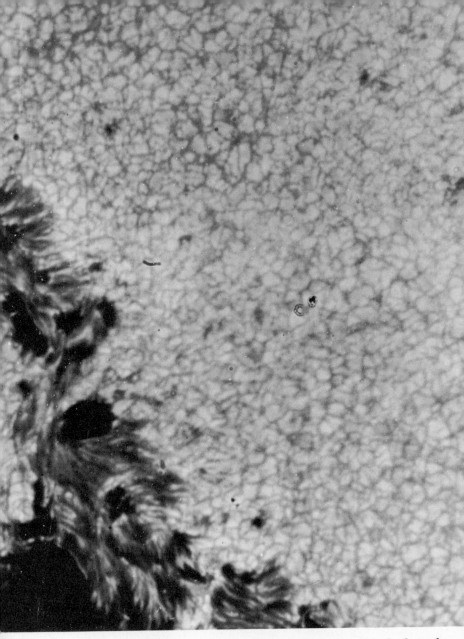

Ill. 71. Granulation of the solar surface (similar to cumulus clouds in the terrestrial atmosphere but much hotter), photographed from a rocket shot into the stratosphere. (*Project Stratoscope of Princeton University, sponsored by the Office of Naval Research and the National Science Foundation, with additional support from NASA.*)

the Sun resembles the boiling lava in the crater of an active volcano; it swirls and spurts in violent, turbulent motion. Rapid fluctuation of local brightness caused by the streams of hot gases rising from the solar interior and sinking back under the surface makes the solar surface look like a fine network of light and shadow known as "granulation." Now and then particularly large and bright tongues of hot gases known as "flares" break through, rising thousands of miles above the solar surface. During the eclipses, when the bright face of the Sun is completely covered by the body of the Moon, one can observe these flares in profile as giant tongues of flame shooting out into space. In olden times, solar eclipses presented the only occasions to see these brilliant eruptions, and astronomers traveled to the far corners of the Earth to study them. Nowadays one can do it any time (in the daytime, of course) from any observation point, due to the invention of the so-called "coronagraph," an instrument in which the bright disk of the Sun is artificially obscured by means of an ingenious optical arrangement.

Vast eruptions of hot gases from the Sun's surface are usually associated with sunspots, the darkish areas which seem to represent giant whirlpools of hot gases which may not be unlike the cyclones and hurricanes in the terrestrial atmosphere. The similarity is strengthened by the fact that, as are the atmospheric whirlpools described in the previous chapter, sunspots are confined to the medium latitudes on both sides of the solar equator. One of the riddles concerning sunspots is that their number shows well-defined periodicity in time, with a period of about 11½ years. Illus. 72 shows the record for more than two centuries of the observed number of sunspots; the last maximum occurred in the year 1958, and their number is now on the decrease. These periodic increases and decreases in the number of spots must somehow be connected with events taking place below the visible solar surface, but nobody knows how. The number and intensity of flares and prominences associated with sunspots show a similar periodicity.

A very important discovery concerning sunspots was made some fifty years ago by the American astronomer George E. Hale.

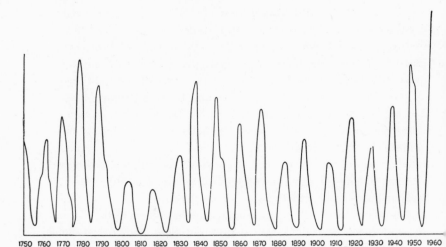

Ill. 72. Periodic changes in the number of sunspots during the last two centuries, according to the records of Zurich Astronomical Observatory.

Analyzing light coming from sunspots, he found evidence of very
strong magnetic fields in those regions. A spectrograph breaks sunlight into a long rainbow-colored ribbon with a large number of
thin black lines crossing it in many places. These Fraunhofer
lines, so called after their discoverer, are due to specific absorption of various wavelengths by the chemical elements present in
the solar atmosphere, and their study gives us invaluable information about the chemical constitution of the Sun and other stars.
In 1896 the Dutch physicist Pieter Zeeman showed that, if a terrestrial source of light, such as a gas flame, is placed between the
poles of a magnet, each line splits into several closely placed components, the distance between which is proportional to the
strength of the magnetic field. Thus, observing the Zeeman effect
in the spectrum of light emitted by distant sources, we may be
able to detect and to measure the magnetic field existing at the
place of its origin. Hale found that Fraunhofer lines in the spectrum of the light coming from sunspots show very strong Zeeman
splitting, which gives evidence of the presence of magnetic fields
thousands of times stronger than the magnetic field of the Earth.

The presence of these magnetic fields, coupled with the fact that, because of exceedingly high temperatures, atoms in the solar atmosphere are broken up into positively and negatively charged ions, turns the motion of the gaseous materials in sunspots into a wild tarantella dance. It is known that electrically charged particles moving through magnetic fields are forced to spiral around the magnetic lines, and that on the other hand magnetic lines would bend and twist depending on electric currents flowing through the gas, and on the motion of the gas masses themselves. Thus, in the whirlpool of hot gases which form a sunspot, there is a continuous interplay of electromagnetic and hydrodynamic forces which makes the entire phenomenon extremely complicated. The shape of hot gas streams, as seen on the photographs of solar prominences, strongly suggests that the motion proceeds along magnetic lines caused by the spiraling currents forming whirlpools. And it is very difficult to say with any degree of certainty what causes what and by which means.

One thing is certain: the sunspots and the flares connected with them are the sources of violent electromagnetic activity which could be detected at interplanetary distances. And indeed, one of the first scientific achievements of radar, a device developed during the Second World War exclusively for military purposes, was the discovery of the so-called "solar noise," i.e., the short radio waves emanating from the surface of the Sun. The intensity of the Sun's broadcasting into the surrounding space is closely correlated with the activity on its surface, and each new bright flare is accompanied by the immediate increase of the solar noise received by radio telescopes. To be more precise, we should say not "immediate" but "eight minutes later" because this is the time taken by all electromagnetic waves (including light waves) to cover the distance separating us from the Sun.

But this is only a part of the story. Most of the material forming the surface of the Sun is hydrogen, the atoms of which are broken up into protons and electrons. Being subjected to rapidly varying magnetic fields, these particles are accelerated in a way similar to that used in various types of particle accelerators ("atom smashers") used in our nuclear laboratories. But whereas

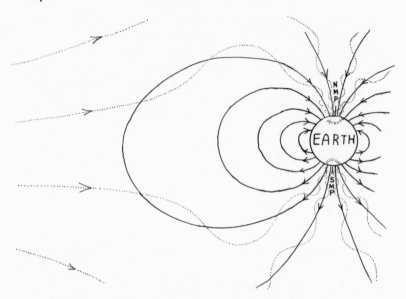

Ill. 73. Motion of electrically charged particles from the Sun in the magnetic
field of the Earth. Solid lines: Earth's magnetic field; dotted lines:
projectories of the particles.

particle accelerators are carefully planned and the motion of accelerated particles is precalculated with great precision, the functioning of solar particle accelerators is still an unsolved problem. The
fact is, however, that powerful streams of protons and electrons
at high velocities are rushing out into space from the surface of
the Sun. The energy carried to the Earth by these particles during
the period of maximum sunspot activity may be as much as 10
per cent of the total energy of sunlight. The number of protons
coming from the Sun to the Earth is extremely large: about 1
billion particles per square centimeter per second. If all protons
which came to the Earth from the Sun during the period of geological history combined with oxygen of terrestrial origin, they
would produce enough water to raise the ocean level by about
50 feet.

When a particularly violent flare shoots high above the surface
of the Sun, powerful streams of high-energy protons and electrons

start toward the Earth. The fastest of them arrive within a few hours, whereas the slower ones may take a day or two for the journey. Having been produced by strong magnetic fields in the sunspots, the swarms of oncoming charged particles have now to cope with the magnetic field of the Earth. The lines of forces of the terrestrial magnetic field diverge from the south magnetic pole in the Antarctic, arch around the body of the Earth, and converge on the north magnetic pole in the Boothia peninsula in northern Canada. As we have said, electrically charged particles moving through a magnetic field are forced to spiral around the lines of forces, thus following their general direction.

A glance at the diagram (Illus. 73) of the magnetic field which surrounds the Earth shows that the beams of particles which were originally flying in parallel trajectories all the way from the Sun to the Earth are deflected by the terrestrial magnetic field toward the north and south poles, and enter the atmosphere in the Arctic and Antarctic regions. The fastest of them penetrate in large quantities all the way to the bottom of the ionosphere, and increase quite considerably the ionization of air normally maintained by the ultraviolet rays of the Sun. The air in these regions becomes much more electrically conductive and, instead of reflecting radio waves, it begins to absorb them. This causes the so-called "radio blackouts": the electromagnetic waves sent out by the broadcasting stations are almost completely absorbed in their first encounter with the ionospheric layers, and nothing is reflected back to the ground. Long-range radio communication on the surface of the Earth becomes completely disrupted for hours or days until the ionosphere comes back again to its normal state.

Because of the change of electrical conditions in the ionosphere, powerful electric currents begin to flow through it, producing magnetic fields which overlap the normal magnetic field of the Earth, which is caused by electric currents in its molten interior. Compass needles go wild, pointing in different directions every minute, and we speak about a magnetic storm.

The swarms of electrically charged particles from the Sun are also responsible for the beautiful optical displays known as the *aurora borealis*, or *polar lights*. Just as electrons flying through a tube of an ordinary fluorescent lamp or of a neon advertising sign cause the atoms of rarefied gas in these tubes to emit characteristic light, rarefied air in the ionosphere becomes luminous when the streams of charged particles from the Sun pass through it. Long curtains glowing with greenish and reddish light hang in the sky above our heads. They move and wave, following the capricious behavior of the incoming particle streams and the air motion in the ionosphere. Spectroscopic studies of light emitted by auroras indicate the presence of three elements: nitrogen, oxygen, and hydrogen. While the first two represent the main components of air, the hydrogen atoms must be formed from protons that have arrived from the Sun.

Speaking about sunspots, we have mentioned the interesting, but as yet unexplained, fact that their number periodically increases and decreases with an average period of 11½ years. This periodicity is reflected in all terrestrial phenomena which depend on solar activity. The rate of occurrence of magnetic storms, radio blackouts, and auroras goes in step with the number of sunspots. There is a perfect correlation between the number of sunspots and the Hudson's Bay Company records of the number of silver fox skins bought from the hunters every year since the foundation of the company: the more sunspots, the better the trade. This surprising correlation may possibly be explained by saying that bright auroras during long polar nights help the hunters to get their fox. There have been many efforts to establish more mysterious correlations between the periodicity of sunspots and such different phenomena as the arrival of starlings in spring, the fluctuations of the stock market, and social revolutions.

MAGNETOSPHERE (A NEW ONE!)

At altitudes of a few thousand miles, where the artificial satellites fly, there is no air at all and the man-made little moons cruising at these altitudes fly through what can be called practically empty space. But this does not mean at all that the influence of the Earth stops at these distances. In fact, as has been found during recent years, our Earth rules the vacuum surrounding it through its magnetic field, which extends far beyond the conventional limits of the terrestrial atmosphere. Information concerning these altitudes was obtained by means of particle counters carried by rockets which probed the space around our planet up to distances of many tens of thousands of miles. It was collected mostly by a team of American scientists led by an Iowa University professor, James Van Allen.

The most striking results were obtained from the flight of Pioneer III (December 6, 1958) which was supposed to reach the Moon, but did not quite make it and fell back toward the Earth after soaring more than 65,000 miles (16 times the Earth's radius) out into space. The findings of particle counters carried by that rocket were transmitted back to Earth, providing the unexpected information that both on the way up and on the way down the rocket passed through two regions of extremely strong high-energy radiation. The first maximum of radiation intensity was reached at 2000 miles (½ of the Earth's radius) above the ground; the second, and considerably more intensive one, at about 10,000 miles (2½ times the Earth's radius). The intensity of radiation which exists in these regions may be as high as 100 roentgens per hour, a "roentgen" being the standard unit for measuring the amount of high-energy radiation. The lethal dose of radiation for a human being is assumed to be about 800 roentgens, and much smaller amounts than that will cause irreparable damage to the reproductive system and result in many harmful mutations in the children, and the children's children, of a person exposed to it. The existence of these regions of high radiation intensity surrounding our globe spells serious practical difficulties for the would-be astronauts planning to fly away from the Earth for a visit to the Moon and the planets of the solar system.

But from the purely scientific point of view Van Allen's radiation belts are of great help for understanding the Earth-Sun electromagnetic relationship. As we have discussed earlier, high-energy protons and electrons originating in sunspots and arriving at the Earth are deflected by the terrestrial magnetic field to the polar regions and enter the atmosphere mostly in the Arctic and

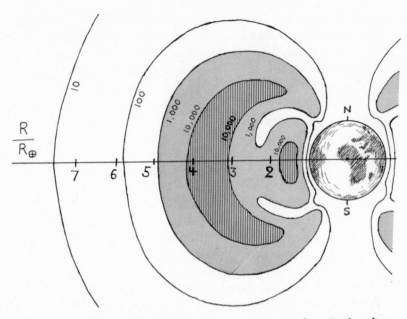

Ill. 74. Van Allen radiation belts. Distances are expressed in Earth radius
R⊕. Figures show radiation intensity in arbitrary units. (Studies conducted
late in 1962 have modified these findings somewhat.)

the Antarctic regions. It seems now that besides just deflecting
the incoming beams of charged particles, the magnetic field of
the Earth also provides a mechanism for trapping them tempo-
rarily in the regions high above the outer limits of the atmosphere.
As can be shown by rather complicated mathematical calculations, the corkscrew-shaped trajectory of the particle will be reversed at the points where the magnetic lines of forces comes
close together, so that the particle will move back and forth between these two points. At the same time this trajectory will drift
slowly around the Earth in a westerly direction for protons and
an easterly direction for electrons, thus forming the doughnut-
shaped radiation belts around the Earth. A provisional map of
these belts (and we do not know why there are two of them) is
shown in Illus. 74. It can be noticed that the northern and southern "horns" of the most intensive outer radiation belt come com-

paratively close to the surface of the Earth just above the regions in which polar lights are usually observed. It may well be that some of the particles caught in the Van Allen belt leak out through these horns and penetrate into the ionosphere, causing polar-light display.

Although the picture of the space environment of our globe is becoming clearer and clearer, owing to the discoveries of recent years, an immense amount of work still has to be done before it will be completely understood.

8

Nature and Origin of Life

BASIC FACTS ABOUT LIFE

LIVING BEINGS like ourselves, cats, canaries, rhinoceroses, rose-bushes, and palm trees are highly organized communities of billions of elementary units known as living cells. And just as in human communities we encounter people engaged in different occupations, being farmers, musicians, policemen, carpenters, scientists, plumbers, nurses, etc., the cells forming a living organism have many specialized functions. Among the many types of animal and plant cells are digestive cells lining the walls of the intestines, muscle cells providing locomotion, nerve cells serving as an intercommunication system, root cells sucking water and salts from the soil, green leaf cells assimilating carbon dioxide from the air, and, above all, reproductive cells securing the survival of the species.

There are also more rudimentary cellular communities in which no specialization takes place, such as, for example, the corals and sponges. Finally there are hermit cells, which prefer to live all alone, such as amoebas, green algae, and various types of bacteria.

But, no matter whether a given cell belongs to a highly organized community or lives all alone, it always has the same basic characteristics. It is always a tiny lump of jelly-like material known as *cytoplasm*, containing within itself a still smaller lump known as the *cellular nucleus*.

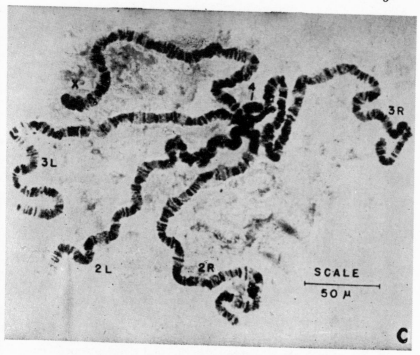

Ill. 75. Photomicrograph of female larva *Drosophila melanogaster*. X, the X chromosomes, closely paired, side by side; 2L and 2R, the left and right limb of the paired second chromosomes; 3L and 3R, the third chromosomes; 4, the fourth chromosomes. *(From* Drosophila Guide, *by M. Demerec and B. P. Kaufmann, Washington, Carnegie Foundation of Washington, 1945. Used by permission of Mr. Demerec)*

If we compare a cell with a factory producing various chemical materials necessary for the maintenance and the development of a living organism, the nucleus should be compared with the manager's office, which issues instructions as to what should be produced and how to produce it. Cellular nuclei contain long thin threads known as *chromosomes*, which play the role of the file cabinets in the manager's office; they contain all the production plans and blueprints (Illus. 75). When a cell is getting ready to divide, each of its chromosomes breaks up lengthwise into two identical threads. One of these threads is pulled to one end of the cell, while its counterpart is pulled to another end. A wall grows between the two parts, and the mother cell is neatly divided into two daughter cells, the nuclei of which carry information identical to that of the mother cell, determining their task in life.

The main body of the cell in our factory analogy, i.e., the cytoplasm, can be compared with the machinery and workers carrying out the production job according to instructions received from the manager's office. The cytoplasm contains complex chemical materials known as enzymes which perform many different tasks necessary for the development and survival of the organism. There are digestive enzymes which break up the foodstuff into simpler units to be used later for building new substances essential for the organism. There are enzymes whose task is to extract energy from the foodstuff and to store it until it is needed for locomotion and many other diverse activities of organisms. There are enzymes which synthesize from the broken foodstuff fragments such necessary substances as milk for feeding progeny, purple pigment necessary for color vision, or dark pigment for hair or skin coloring. There are thousands of different enzymes which control the life and development of any living organism.

In recent decades scientists have been coming closer and closer to an understanding of life on the "molecular level," i.e., to explaining various biological phenomena on the basis of detailed knowledge of the structure of various complex chemical molecules which form living organisms. The molecules of inorganic substances are usually very simple. Thus, a molecule of water consists of two atoms of hydrogen and one atom of oxygen; a molecule of table salt consists of one atom of sodium and one atom of chlorine; and a molecule of quartz consists of one silicon atom and two oxygen atoms. Molecules which play the principal roles in the structure of living organisms are immensely more complex and consist of millions of individual atoms. What makes the study of these complex molecules comparatively easy is the fact that they can be considered as long sequences of just a few rather simple units arranged in a specific order characteristic for each

Ill. 76. A model of a protein molecule. *(Courtesy of Dr. Barbara Low, Columbia University)*

particular molecule. It turns out that there are two quite different kinds of these long organic molecules: 1) *proteins*, which (apart from bones, fat, etc.) constitute the major part of all living organisms; 2) *nucleic acids* (about one teaspoonful of them in a man), which form chromosomes and are responsible for the transfer of hereditary properties of the organisms.

THE PROTEINS

Let us start with the proteins, which have been the subject of intensive biochemical studies since the beginning of the present

Ill. 77. Three amino acids (glycine, alanine, and cysteine) arranged in sequence within a long protein molecule.

century. If we look at a protein molecule through an electron microscope, which permits much higher magnifications than its optical counterpart, we see long thin threads without any apparent inner structure. Chemical studies indicate, however, that these threads are formed by sequences of a very large number of comparatively simple molecules known as "amino acids" and on the basis of chemical analysis one can construct exact models of protein molecules (Illus. 76). There are twenty different amino acids which participate in the structure of various protein molecules, and the order in which they are arranged in the sequence determines the function which the protein in question is supposed to carry out. The situation is quite similar to a cookbook containing large numbers of different recipes: how to cook an omelet, a cherry pie, clam chowder, meat loaf, etc. Each recipe contains the same letters in about the same proportion, the only difference being the order in which these letters are arranged to form words and sentences. When biochemists determined how the amino acids were lined up in different protein molecules, they learned that very small changes in that order led to an entirely different activity of the protein in question. Thus, for example, all mam-

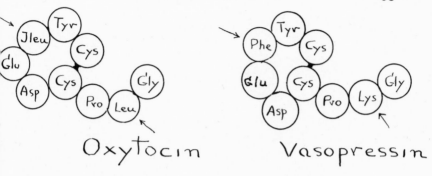

Ill. 78. Structural formula for two simple proteins, according to Vincent du Vigneaud. They differ only in two amino acids (indicated by arrows).

mals possess glands which secrete into the bloodstream two hormones known as *oxytocin* and *vasopressin*. Each of these hormones is a protein molecule formed by a sequence of nine amino acids, and the only difference between the two sequences is in the third and the eighth link of the chain (Illus. 78). Yet, in spite of this small difference, these two protein molecules exert entirely different effects on the organism in which they are produced. Oxytocin, secreted into the bloodstream of expectant mothers, stimulates the production of milk by the breast glands, and causes the contraction of the uterus which results in the birth of the offspring. Vasopressin, on the other hand, causes contraction of the blood vessels, which results in increased blood pressure. Thus, the change of only two out of nine "letters" in nature's "recipe book" leads to strikingly different results!

A somewhat more complicated protein molecule is that of *insulin* (which is composed of fifty-one amino-acid units, arranged in a somewhat complicated looping sequence (Illus. 79). Insulin has the important function of extracting energy from the sugar consumed by the living organism and storing it until the time it is needed. To carry out this function, the insulin molecule must be constructed exactly as is shown in Illus. 79. If, because of some mistake in the insulin-producing glands, the order of amino acids is different from what it should be, the defective insulin molecules will not be successful in their job, and the or-

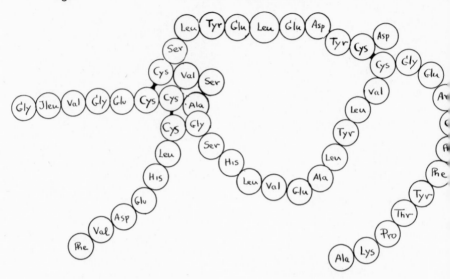

Ill. 79. Structural formula of insulin, according to Frederick Sanger. It consists of two sequences of 21 and 30 amino acids respectively. Black bridges between the cystine (Cys) pairs represent the sulfur bonds which give to protein molecules their grotesque shapes. Similar sulfur bonds show in the structure of oxytocin and vasopressin.

ganism (human or animal) which has that bad luck becomes a diabetic.

The few examples we have given are intended to illustrate the fact that all vital functions of a living organism are regulated by the detailed chemical structure of the protein molecules forming it. And, just as a misprint in the cookbook may result in producing an uneatable dish, a mistake in the protein structure may lead to disease and the death of a living organism.

NUCLEIC ACIDS

As we have stated, nucleic-acid molecules constitute a very small fraction of the living organism; there is just about one tea-

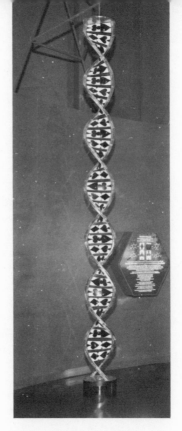

Ill. 80. A photomicrograph of DNA molecules. *(Courtesy of Dr. Robley Williams, University of California)*

Ill. 81. A model of the DNA molecule, with playing-card suits representing four nucleotides.

spoonful in a man. But, though they are in such an extreme minority, these molecules play an exceedingly important part in life. They are responsible for carrying and propagating all the hereditary information of the organism in question. The facts that a baby grows up into a human being, that a puppy develops into a dog, and that an appleseed gives rise to an apple tree, are due to differences between the nucleic-acid molecules inside the cellular nuclei of these particular species. Just as in the case of protein molecules, the molecules of nucleic acids are seen through an electron microscope as long threads somewhat thicker than proteins (Illus. 80), but their structure is quite different. Instead of twenty different units, as in proteins, nucleic acids are composed of only four different units, which are known as *nucleotides*.

In the nucleic acid found in the cell nucleus, called deoxyribo-
nucleic acid (DNA), the four nucleotides are arranged in a double-
helix sequence, and are known as adenine, guanine, cytosine, and
thymine. The first three of these are also constituents of the
single-stranded molecules of *ribonucleic acid* (RNA), found outside the nucleus in the cell's cytoplasm, but in RNA the fourth
nucleotide, thymine, is replaced by uracil.

It will simplify the discussion if we call the four nucleotides
hearts, diamonds, spades, and clubs, referring to the four suits of
playing cards. In the first sequence, the nucleotides can be arranged in any arbitrary order such as: ♦ ♥ ♠ ♥ ♣ ♦ ♥ ♠, etc.
and the order in which they follow one another determines
whether the organism is a human being, a dog, or an apple tree.
The second sequence of nucleotides, which runs alongside the
first one, is completely defined by it. In fact, hearts always pair
with clubs, and spades with diamonds. Thus, in our example, the
two sequences look like this:

♦ ♥ ♠ ♥ ♣ ♦, etc.
♠ ♣ ♦ ♣ ♥ ♠, etc.

Each of the four nucleotides is a comparatively simple chemical
molecule composed of carbon, nitrogen, oxygen, hydrogen, and

Ill. 82. Section of DNA chain showing four nucleotides which form a back-
bone chain of sugar molecules. The nucleotide containing adenine is repre-

phosphorus atoms, and, in recent years, biochemists have been able to find out how these five kinds of atoms are put together. Illus. 82 shows the structural formula of a section of a double-stranded nucleic-acid molecule. Cumbersome as it looks, this molecule is actually quite simple, being formed by the monotonous repetition of various nucleotide pairs, which we symbolized earlier in the text by the pairs of playing cards. And, as has already been mentioned, the order in which various pairs follow one another determines completely all the properties of the organism to which it belongs.

The double-stranded structure of DNA molecules is a feature which is absolutely necessary for the process of cell division and the propagation of species. Before a cell divides into two, each double-stranded molecule of DNA in its nucleus splits lengthwise into two single strands. This splitting is then followed by the regeneration of each of the two strands, which is accomplished by capturing free nucleotides present in abundance in the nuclear fluid at that time. Since hearts can capture only diamonds, spades only clubs, etc., the two regenerated double-stranded molecules are identical with the original one. After this is done, the pair of daughter molecules travel to opposite ends of the cell, carrying the original hereditary information.

sented by spades, cystosine by hearts, guanine by diamonds, and thymine by clubs.

PROTEIN SYNTHESIS

As has been mentioned, the molecules of nucleic acid carry in a coded form a complete set of instructions pertaining to the properties of the organism in question, while protein molecules receive these instructions and use them in their task of biosynthesis of the various substances necessary for life processes. How is this done? Although we still do not know all the details of that complicated process, we can formulate some basic arithmetical relations between arrangement of nucleotides in nucleic-acid molecules, and that of amino acids in proteins. Using again our playing-card analogy, let us imagine a simplified poker game in which only aces are used and each player is dealt only three cards. How many different hands can one get in that case? First, one can have three identical cards: three hearts, three diamonds, etc. This makes four different possibilities. Then one can have one pair of identical cards with the third one different, as for example two diamonds and one spade. Since we have four choices for the pair, and only three choices left for the third card, the total number of possibilities is $4 \times 3 = 12$. Finally, one can have all three cards different, and, depending on which is missing, we have again four possibilities. Thus, the total number of different combinations is $4 + 12 + 4 = 20$, i.e., exactly the number of different amino acids that participate in the protein structure.

On the basis of this analogy it is reasonable to conclude that each amino acid in the protein molecule is defined by a *triplet* of nucleotides in the molecule of nucleic acid. As proteins are synthesized in the cytoplasm of the cell which contains RNA, presumably different amino-acid molecules have a definite affinity for the triplets of RNA nucleotides, and arrange themselves alongside the RNA molecules in the order which is defined by the order of the nucleotides forming it. Thus, by this strictly deterministic process, proteins synthesized within the cell of a given organism are formed exactly according to the instructions carried by the RNA molecules contained in their cytoplasm, which in their turn, have a structure determined exactly by nuclear DNA.

This scheme of basic processes taking place in a living cell leads the scientists working in this field to an unshakable conclusion that all manifestations of life can be reduced, at least in principle, to chemical reactions between rather complicated nucleic acid and protein molecules from which all the living organisms are built.

The final step in decoding protein sequences was made in 1961, by the team of Marshall W. Nirenberg and J. Henrich Matthaei at the National Institute of Arthritis and Metabolic Diseases, and independently by Severo Ochoa and his co-workers at the New York University School of Medicine. It was found that if one uses a synthetic nucleic acid formed by a sequence of identical nucleotides, only one particular amino acid is incorporated into the protein structure. Thus, for example, nucleic-acid molecules formed exclusively from uracil:

U U U U U U U U . . .

produced proteins formed exclusively from phenylalanine:

Phe Phe Phe Phe . . .

Proceeding in that way, the biochemists were able to establish the relation between different amino acids and the nucleotide triplets necessary for incorporating them into protein molecules. Their results are given in the table below, in which A stands for adenine, G for guanine, C for cytosine, and U for uracil:

Amino Acid	Nucleotide Triplet	Amino Acid	Nucleotide Triplet
Phenylalanine	UUU	Isoleucine	UUA
Alanine	UCG	Leucine	UUC, UUG, UUA
Arginine	UCG	Lysine	UAA
Aspartic Acid	UAG	Methionine	UAG
Asparagine	UAA, UAC	Proline	UCC
Cysteine	UUG	Serine	UUC
Glutamic Acid	UAG	Threonine	UAC, UCC
Glutamine		Tryptophan	UGG
(predicted)	UCG	Tyrosine	UUA
Glycine	UGG	Valine	UUG
Histidine	UAC		

Thus, after almost a decade of struggle, the secret RNA code

202 A Planet Called Earth

which transfers the hereditary information from nucleic acids inside a cellular nucleus to the enzymes in its cytoplasm was finally broken!

SIMPLEST LIVING BEINGS

If one were to attempt to explain the principles of radio to somebody unfamiliar with them, it would be a poor plan to bring that person to a modern broadcasting station with thousands of complicated electronic gadgets. A much better plan would be to present that person with a do-it-yourself radio kit based on the same principles but much simpler. Similarly, in order to understand the "riddle of life" it would be unwise to start with such complex organisms as human beings or any of the higher animals and plants. A much better understanding of the basic processes of life can be obtained by the study of the simplest living beings, which carry out the same basic living processes, without the burden of very complex organization.

Such "simplest living beings" are represented by the so-called *viruses*, which are so small that they cannot be seen through even the best optical microscope. The use of the much more powerful electron-microscope gives us the chance, however, to see their shape and to study their properties. Illus. 83 shows a photograph of the *tobacco-mosaic virus*, which imperils thousands of acres of tobacco plantations.

Like any other living organism, viruses are composed of nucleic-acid and protein molecules. What we see in the electron-micrographs are the protein skins of these unpleasant little creatures. The nucleic-acid molecules, which determine the nature of any given virus and what animal or plant it will attack, are hidden in its interior. The way a virus attacks its victim, be it a man or a tobacco plant, is quite simple. It attaches itself to the outer wall of the cell, and, while the protein skin is left outside, the nucleic acid is injected into the cell's interior. And then comes a big battle! The nucleic acids in the cell's chromosomes send out instructions to the proteins forming the cell's body to "carry

Ill. 83. Living molecules? The particles of tobacco-mosaic virus magnified 34,800 times. This picture was taken by means of an electron microscope. *(Photographed by Dr. G. Oster and Dr. W. M. Stanley)*

on" in the same way as they did before the invasion, and to perform the functions proper to the cell of the species in question. On the other hand, the invading nucleic-acid molecules of the virus want the proteins of the body cell to change their "political affiliation" and to start producing new viruses. If the invading virus wins the battle, a hundred new viruses are formed in the cell's body from the material which was originally earmarked for normal cell growth and replication. The cell's wall deteriorates, and the newly formed viruses attack the neighboring cells, causing further damage.

Unpleasant as the viruses are, they give great help to biologists in the understanding of the basic processes of life, and in 1955 two American biochemists, Heinz Fraenklin-Conrat and Robley Williams, working at the Virus Institute of the University of California, performed an exciting experiment which (with certain restrictions) can be described as the "artificial production" of a living organism. Working with the tobacco-mosaic virus, they found a way by chemical means to separate the nucleic acid forming its interior from the protein forming its skin. As a result they obtained, in one tube, a water solution of nucleic acid and, in another, that of the protein. The molecules of the two substances appeared to be exactly like non-living, though complex, organic molecules extracted from other materials, and gave no manifestation of life whatsoever. However, when the two solutions were put together, the protein molecules started to wind around the molecules of amino acids, and a short time thereafter the electron-microscope showed the presence of the typical tobacco-mosaic viruses. When these "recreated" viruses were applied to the leaves of a tobacco plant, they began to multiply as if nothing had happened, and the entire plant was soon the victim of the mosaic disease.

Of course, one can make two objections to calling this the artificial production of life. First, the nucleic-acid and protein molecules used in these experiments were not synthesized from basic chemical elements, but obtained by breaking up the living virus. Second, viruses are the simplest living creatures; what about making a kitten or a baby? The answers to these questions are: first, that great advances have been made during the last few years in synthesizing proteins and nucleic acids from elements, and, although today we cannot make such long sequences as those encountered in viruses, it certainly will be possible in the future; second, that one does not need to synthesize a kitten; all that is needed is to synthesize an ovum and a sperm, which are not much more complex structures than viruses.

THE ORIGIN OF LIFE

The problem of the origin of life on our planet begins with the question of how the proteins and the nucleic acids, these two basic chemicals which form all living beings, could have originated under normal conditions on the surface of the Earth. A good organic chemist today can synthesize all twenty amino acids and the four nucleotides of RNA or of DNA without much difficulty; but how could these substances have originated under natural conditions?

A brilliant idea as to how this could have happened was expressed several years ago by Harold Urey, whose name we have already mentioned. Urey's idea is based on the modern theory of the origin of the planetary system (Chapter 1), according to which protoplanets possessed originally extensive atmospheres formed mostly by hydrogen and by hydrogen compounds such as *methane* (CH_4), *ammonia* (NH_3) and *water vapor* (OH_2). Chemical elements in these compounds (i.e., hydrogen, carbon, nitrogen, and oxygen) are exactly those which form the amino acids and the long protein molecules. Urey theorized that, when subjected to the ultraviolet radiation of the sun, and the electric discharges resulting from thunderstorms in the terrestrial atmosphere, the molecules of these simple compounds could unite to form more complex molecules of various amino acids. To confirm his ideas, he asked one of his students, Stanley L. Miller, to carry out an experiment in which a mixture of hydrogen, methane, ammonia, and water vapor in a test tube was subjected for several days to a slow electric discharge. When the contents of the test tube were finally analyzed, they revealed the presence of several amino acids normally found in proteins, thus constituting a brilliant confirmation of Urey's hypothesis. Presumably, during the early existence of our planet, while it still had an atmosphere consisting of hydrogen and hydrogen compounds, amino acids were continuously produced in that atmosphere and were slowly precipitated down to the ground, forming a rather concentrated solution in the ocean waters (those which landed on the continents were probably also washed into the ocean by rains). This process provided one chemical component essential for life.

Much less is known about the origin of another component, the nucleic acid without which life cannot exist. The molecular chains of DNA and RNA contain atoms of phosphorus, which are not likely to be found in the atmosphere. Also, in synthesizing these compounds one needs high temperatures rather than ultraviolet radiation or electric discharges. One of the bold hypotheses proposed in this direction suggests that nucleotides were produced as the result of the activity of underwater volcanoes, but, so far, it still remains a bold hypothesis.

The next problem, of course, is how the solution of amino acids and nucleotides in the ocean waters evolved into the proteins and amino acids which united to form the first living organism capable of reproduction. We know this did happen during the geological eras which may have preceded the Cambrian period (first fossils) by a few billions of years.

Discussing the origin of a planetary system we came to the conclusion that it is a rather common event and that a great many stars most likely possess planetary systems similar to ours. And we have also seen that it would be natural to expect the formation, in the atmospheres of such planets, of chemical compounds essential for building living matter. Thus it seems very likely that life similar to ours flourishes on billions of other planets circling the stars which form the system of the Milky Way.

9

The Evolution of Life

CAUSES OF ORGANIC EVOLUTION

WE, THE PEOPLE of the Earth, consider ourselves, and quite justly, the crown of creation. Nature worked hard for billions of years to build, from the simple organic molecules which were formed on the Earth's surface or in its atmosphere when it was still quite young, complex organisms like the one who wrote these lines and those who are reading them. What were the factors responsible for the organic evolution which led to the immense variety of living beings and to the almost unbelievable complexity of their individual structure? Early in the nineteenth century the French botanist Jean Baptiste Pierre Antoine, Chevalier de Lamarck, proposed a theory which, though completely obsolete now, is still believed by Soviet Russia's botanist Academician Trofim Denisovitch Lysenko. According to Lamarck, the evolutionary progress of living organisms was the result of their continuous adjustment to their environment, the changes taking place during the life of one individual being communicated to its progeny by heredity. Thus, for example, the long neck of the giraffe, as we know the animal today, was supposed to be due to repeated efforts of the members of numerous past generations to stretch their necks in order to snatch leaves from tall palm trees.

In the middle of the nineteenth century Lamarck's views were replaced by those of the famous British zoologist Charles Darwin. According to Darwin, evolutionary changes were not the result of the continuous adjustment of living organisms to their environment, but were rather the results of a blind "trial and error" process in which the errors were ruthlessly exterminated in the struggle for existence. Darwin argued that fertile Mother Nature always overproduces the progeny of all living organisms to such an extent that, if unchecked, their number will grow beyond any limit, so that there soon will be insufficient space and food for them. This circumstance results naturally in the struggle for existence, and in this struggle the fittest organisms survive, while those less fit perish. The second part of Darwin's argument was that the offspring, be they puppies, kittens, cubs, fledglings, or saplings, are always slightly different from one another and from their parents. Some of these differences may be helpful in the struggle for existence, whereas the majority are harmful. The process of natural selection results in the survival of the fittest, who pass their properties to their offspring and their offspring's offspring, thus leading to a gradual improvement of subsequent generations. In contrast to Lamarck's peaceful adjustment process, Darwin's evolution mechanism requires the sacrifice of many offspring for the improvement of a few.

We know today that Darwin was absolutely correct in his assumption concerning the variability of the properties of the offspring. In fact, as we have seen in the previous chapter, all hereditary properties of any given living organism are determined by the order in which the four different molecular units, known as nucleotides, are arranged in the long nucleic-acid threads which form the chromosomes. As the result of thermal motion and the action of various types of radiation coming from outside, some of these units may be dislocated, changing the original order. Such dislocations result in jumplike changes of hereditary characteristics known as *mutations*, which are carried by a chromosomal replication mechanism to all future generations. Old man Darwin would be very glad to learn that the small occasional changes, the existence of which he postulated in his theory of evolution, are in fact often quite large, such as the change in the color of the fruit-fly's eye from black to red, or changes in the shape and color of ears of corn.

There is hardly any doubt that Darwin's "struggle for existence" principle operated very early in the evolution of life on the Earth, at the time when the most complex organic "beings" were simple proteins formed by polymerization (sticking together) of various amino acids dissolved in the ocean waters. In fact, one can trace Darwin's evolutionary principle all the way down to simple inorganic reactions. If one exposes a mixture of powdered iron and silver metals to the action of oxygen, more iron oxides than silver oxides will be produced because the oxidation of iron proceeds at a faster rate than that of silver. Similarly, various more complicated chemical processes must have been going on between the protein molecules dissolved in the water of primordial oceans, with the result that those molecules whose reactions were intrinsically faster had the upper edge over the other, slower ones. This early development of life, or rather of organic matter, is hidden from us behind a heavy curtain of mystery because no biochemical fossils could have been left in the sedimentary rocks of those periods. We also do not know when and how the growing organic molecules acquired the property of replication, i.e., the ability to produce other molecules with the same chemical properties.

THE FIRST STEPS OF ORGANIC EVOLUTION

Since the earliest forms of life were limited to miniature soft-bodied organisms, there is not much chance of finding any extensive evidence of these first living beings among the early fragmented pages of the "Book of Sediments." There is, however, an abundance of indirect evidence. As we have said, the thick layers of marble found in various places on the Earth represent strongly metamorphosed deposits of ordinary limestone, formed probably more than a billion years ago. It is well established at present that the more recent deposits of limestone are due largely to the work of simple micro-organisms, so that we may conclude with some degree of certainty that such simple forms of organic life were already in existence in that distant past.

The deposits formed during these early epochs of the Earth's history also contain a certain amount of carbon in the form of thin graphite layers. Although the presence of carbon can also be attributed to volcanic activity, its distribution through the rocks makes it more likely that it originated as the result of the decay of organic matter and was metamorphized into graphite when the deposits were pushed deeper into the Earth and became subject to very high pressures and temperatures. All this indicates that life was present in its elementary forms more than a couple of billion years ago, and that the absence of "true" fossils, such as we find in the later deposits, is simply due to the fact that at this early stage of development living organisms did not yet have rigid skeletons which could have made lasting impressions on the folded pages of the book of the Earth's history.

If through some miraculous device we were able to move back in time and transport ourselves to a few billion years ago, the ocean water and the rocky slopes of the primeval continental massifs would afford us a rather lifeless view. Only through careful study would we be able to find that life was already present on the surface of the planet, and that numerous micro-organisms of many different kinds were hard at work in their fight for existence. At this early stage of the evolution of our planet the ground was still rather warm, and a large part of the water that now fills the ocean basins was still in the atmosphere, forming a thick layer of heavy clouds. No direct sunlight could penetrate to the surface of the Earth, and the life that was able to exist in this damp darkness must necessarily have been limited to certain micro-organisms that could live and grow entirely without sunlight. Some of these primitive organisms used as their nourishment the remainder of the organic substances dissolved in ocean waters, whereas others grew accustomed to purely inorganic food. This second class of "mineral-eating" organisms can still be found in the so-called "sulfur and iron bacteria," which obtain their vital energy through the oxidation of inorganic compounds of sulfur and iron.* The activity of such bacteria plays quite an important role in the development of the Earth's surface; the iron bacteria, in particular, are probably wholly responsible for the thick deposits of bog iron ore, the main source of iron in the world.

As time went on, the surface of the Earth grew cooler and cooler, more and more water accumulated in the oceans, and the heavy clouds hiding the Sun gradually thinned out. Under the action of the Sun's rays, which now were falling abundantly on the surface of our planet, the primitive micro-organisms were slowly developing the very useful substance chlorophyll to decompose the carbon dioxide of the air and using the carbon thus obtained to build up the organic substances needed for their growth. This possibility of "feeding on the air" opened up new horizons for the development of organic life and, combined with the *principle of collective life,*† culminated in the present highly developed and complex forms of the plant kingdom.

But some of the primitive organisms had chosen another way of development and, instead of getting their food directly from the air, of which there was plenty for everyone, preferred to obtain their carbon compounds in the "ready-to-use" form as produced by laborious plants. Since this parasitic manner of feeding was considerably simpler, the surplus energy of these organisms went into the development of an ability to move, which was quite necessary in order to get the food. Not being satisfied with a purely vegetable diet, the parasitic branch of living things began to eat one another, and the necessity of catching prey or of running away from pursuit developed their locomotive ability to the high degree characterizing the present animal world. The most primitive locomotion device, developed by the cephalopods (the "head-legged" animals) of the early Silurian period and retained until the present day by the squids, was based on the

---

* The existence of such bacteria requires the presence of oxygen in the air, of course.

† I.e., the formation of complex organisms composed of many cells living together.

Ill. 84. A piece of sandstone dating back to the Cambrian period (*ca.* 450,-000,000 B.C.). The tracks seen on its surface are not due to a prehistoric automobile, but were produced by large worms crawling across the wet sand. Note the markings left by the waves. *(Courtesy of the U.S. National Museum)*

simple rocket principle. The spindle-shaped body of these animals is enclosed in a muscular fold of body wall known as the mantle, which leaves, however, some space that can be filled with water. Relaxation of the mantle permits the ingress of water into this cavity, and this water can be ejected in a powerful stream by a rapid muscular contraction, propelling the animal backward at rather high speed. The rocket principle did not prove to be very successful, however, and most organisms developed another method for propelling themselves through the lateral undulations of their elongated bodies. This mechanism reached a high degree of perfection rather early in the development of the inhabitants of marine and terrestrial waters, and only such reactionary animals as the squids still stick to the old principle. It may be noticed, though, that even the squids today possess two horizontal stabilizer fins, which are used for slow forward swimming by means of wavelike undulations.

It must be clear that swift motion through the water could

hardly be achieved in the case of soft-bodied and easily deformable animals, since such motion requires rather rigid stream-
lined shapes, and the work of muscles can be much better trans-
ferred to the water through rigid "moving parts." Another advantage gained by the development of rigid parts of the body was
protection from the attack of another "meat-eating" animal, as
well as better means for attacking the others. These advantages,
combined with the struggle for life and the survival of the fittest,
finally resulted in the transformation of the soft jelly-like forms
of the animal world into the heavily armored types with powerful claws, such as the crabs and lobsters of today. The development of rigid parts turned out to be not only of great help to the
animals themselves, but also to the modern paleontologists, who
look for such remains in the pages of the "Book of Sediments."
Whereas information about the soft-bodied animals of the past
can be collected only from occasional imprints left by them on
soft sand and, through mere chance, preserved to the present
time (see Illus. 84), the animals with rigid shells or skeletons can
be studied from their fossils almost as well as if they were living
today. The whole historical period of the Earth and of life on
its surface begins, properly speaking, from the time when animals began to develop rigid parts or bodies, and the museums of
today are full of shells and skeletons permitting us to visualize
the life forms of the distant past.

At the beginning of the Paleozoic era, some 500 million years
ago, we find ocean life developed to a comparatively high level.
Walking along the sandy ocean beaches of that time, we would
find bunches of greenish seaweeds thrown up by the waves, and
would be able to make a beautiful collection of seashells in the
very same way that so many people do today. Perhaps we would
not be much surprised to see some strange-looking animals
crawling through the wet sand and distantly reminding us of
the horseshoe crabs of today. These animals, known as *trilobites*
(Illus. 85) and representing one of the highest forms of life in
this distant past, were probably developed from the soft-bodied
segmented worms through the hardening of their skin and the
fusion of separate segments into the head and the body. The first

Ill. 85. Fossils of tribolites in the deposits of the Devonian period (*ca.* 300,-000,000 B.C.) — natural size. *(Courtesy of the U.S. National Museum)*

trilobites were rather small, not much larger than a pinhead, and had very rudimentary bodies with a badly developed eyeless head. Later, however, they made considerable progress, and the deposits of the Ordovician and Silurian periods contain the fossils of more than a thousand highly developed species. At the peak of their career the trilobites attained a length exceeding one foot and possessed very grotesque and highly ornamented bodies. This progress was followed, however, by a rapid decline, and the late Permian deposits contain only a few species of these interesting animals. The final blow to the existence of the trilobitic race was evidently dealt by the revolutionary changes on the Earth's surface, which, as we have seen, took place toward the end of the Permian period. The general elevation of the ground, the recession of the ocean, and the disappearance of interior water basins proved to be too much for these animals, which had ruled the surface of the Earth for more than 200 million years, and the race became completely extinct at the climax of the Appalachian revolution. Some side branch of the primitive trilobite stock must have survived all the dangers of the evolutionary past, however, and, becoming better adapted to surrounding conditions, carried their banners down to the present time. The latest representatives of this ancient branch are often served on our table under the names of shrimps, crabs, lobsters, etc.

Although the trilobites were exclusively marine animals, some of their close relatives, known as *eurypterids,* must have migrated up the rivers and into the interior lakes and developed the habit of living in fresh water. In fact, whereas the earliest eurypterids, small creatures only a few inches long, have been found in the marine deposits of the Late Cambrian period, the fossilized remains of the later and more developed representatives of this race (up to 10 feet long!) are very numerous in the deposits of continental waters formed 100 million years later.

Compared with the ocean, life in the fresh water of rivers and lakes is considerably less quiet and subject to much greater uncertainty. It must often have happened that such continental basins were cut off from their water supply and slowly dried up. Though most of the animals living in such basins must have necessarily perished, there was a bare chance that in some rare cases individuals could adjust themselves to the new conditions and continue their life on the dry land. These descendants of the eurypterid race, forced out of the water by the play of unfavorable circumstances, spread over the surface of the continents and became differentiated into various species of centipedes, millepedes, scorpions, spiders, etc. Later they took to the air, forming a large class of flying insects.

Returning to the ocean of the Early Paleozoic era, we find another entirely different line of evolution (Illus. 86). Instead of growing a rigid outer shell enclosing the soft body from without, a certain group of worms began to develop a stiff internal rod running along the entire body and evidently representing the prototype of the spinal cord in the fishes and higher vertebrates of today. A typical example of this transitional stage between ordinary worms and fish can be seen in the species known as *lancelet,* which exists today and probably represents the direct descendants of the primeval fish stock. These animals of wormlike

Ill. 86. Ocean shore, Early Paleozoic era, strewn with wave-borne seaweed and shells. Long, tubelike forms are Silurian straight-shelled cephalopods; snail-shaped forms are round-shelled cephalopods. Trilobites (lower right) would be seen scurrying across the sand. Though marine life had progressed considerably, the land was virtually uninhabited except for some species of millepedes and scorpions. *(Courtesy of the Field Museum of Natural History)*

appearance differ, however, from ordinary worms in having a cartilaginous rod running along their entire length and minute "gill rods" supporting the side walls of the body. It is believed that the further development of this primitive skeleton culminated in the formation of a spinal cord and ribs, which distinguish all vertebrate animals from the more primitive ones. It is interesting to note in this connection that in sharks, which represent the first "true" fish on record and which were in existence as early as the Silurian period, the continuous spinal rod is only partly replaced by the rings of the cartilage, and that complete replacement is attained only in the later fish species and in other higher vertebrates.

The exit of fishes from the water to dry land and their subsequent transformation into amphibians and reptiles were evidently due to the same combined causes as in the case of the more primitive invertebrates and probably proceeded along the same general lines. This exit must have taken place some time during the beginning of the latter part of the Paleozoic era, since the Upper Devonian and the Lower Carboniferous deposits contain some impressions that have been interpreted as the footprints of primitive amphibians. The fossilized skeletons of these amphibians, abundantly preserved in the Upper Carboniferous and Permian deposits, indicate that they belonged to the now extinct group of heavily armored animals with solidly roofed skulls that earned for them the name of *stegocephalians* (i.e., "roof-headed" animals).

Some of these animals were only a few inches long, whereas others, especially those living during the latter part of the Carboniferous period, attained a length exceeding twenty feet. It is noteworthy that at least some species of stegocephalians had a third eye in the center of the forehead, which can also be found in a very rudimentary form in present-day amphibians and some higher vertebrates.*

But as in the case of so many other animal species, this blooming of the ancient amphibian kingdom was cut short by the increasing cold and dryness of the early stages of the Appalachian revolution, although a few of the species persisted well into the Triassic period. At present the amphibians are represented by comparatively few species of small-sized, humble animals such as frogs, toads, and salamanders. Some of the amphibians, however, must have completely lost their affinity for water and migrated to dry land, giving rise to a large reptilian kingdom that was destined to conquer the continents and rule unchallenged for the next 100 million years.

---

* The vestige of the "third eye" is now represented by the so-called pineal gland in the frontal part of the head.

Ill. 87. Certain Early Permian reptiles resembled today's crocodiles. Others had high, bony dorsal fins, probably for defense. Their feet were at their sides; movement on land was slow and sprawling.

(Courtesy of the Field Museum of Natural History)

The early reptiles were lazy, long-bodied animals, many of them resembling the crocodiles of today. Others had very peculiar shapes, with high bony fins running along their backs and probably serving to defend them from unexpected attack (Illus. 87). All these primeval reptiles, like the reptiles of today, had their feet at their sides and were able to advance only by a rather slow sprawling across the land. Not until the beginning of the Mesozoic era did the reptiles develop an erect posture more adapted to running. This change of posture was probably one of the main reasons that enabled them to conquer the land and retain a dominant position throughout the long middle period of the Earth's history.

Parallel with the exit of animal life from the sea to dry land, and even probably preceding it somewhat, an analogous process was going on in the world of plants. Some of the terrestrial plants must have originated from seaweeds growing along the shorelines within the tidal zone and gradually growing accustomed to the periodic recession of the water. Others stemmed from the fresh-water vegetation that was forced to change its way of life owing to the drying out of the inland basins. The vegetation that first appeared on the surface of the continents was still very similar to the simpler forms previously living in the water, and was chiefly confined to the extensive shallow-water areas and marshlands that were so widespread during the inter-revolutionary periods. The forests of that distant past must have presented a very gloomy and fantastic appearance, consisting almost exclusively of ferns, horsetails, and club mosses, which grew to an enormous size (Illus. 88). All these were the primeval spore plants, carrying neither blooming flowers nor fruits, and it took many hundred millions of years before the primeval plants reached the degree of development to which we are accustomed at present.

Since the vegetation of that time was mostly limited to extensive marshlands, the trunks of the fallen forest giants were usually covered by a layer of water and, decomposing without access to the oxygen of the air, gave rise to rich coal deposits. This process of coal formation continued on an especially large scale during the middle part of the Late Paleozoic era, and among the geologists of today this period (lasting from 285,000,000 to 235,000,000 B.C.) is accordingly known as the *Carboniferous period*.

THE GREAT MIDDLE KINGDOM
OF REPTILES

The Mesozoic era of the Earth's history is characterized by the splendid development of animal life on dry land and by the

Ill. 88. Woods of the Middle Paleozoic era were mostly in marshlands and consisted chiefly of giant horsetails, ferns, and club mosses. Carbonized remains of these forest giants constitute present coal deposits.

(Courtesy of the Field Museum of Natural History)

growth of small reptilian forms into giant monsters, known as *dinosaurs,* which challenge the most vivid imagination. As in the case of so many other forms of life, the race of dinosaurs started its existence in the early Triassic period as a group of comparatively small animals, not exceeding 15 feet in length, and developed in all its splendor only toward the end of the era. The early dinosaurs were rather slenderly built and had muscular hind legs and powerful tails, which aided in balancing the body as they ran. They must have been rather similar in appearance to today's Australian kangaroo, except for the absence of fur and the definitely reptilian shape of the head.

The further development of these primitive Triassic dinosaurs led to a great many other forms, widely differing in size and in habits. The most terrifying representative of this group of animals was the so-called *Tyrannosaurus rex,* a huge carnivorous animal up to 20 feet in height and measuring about 45 feet from the tip of its nose to the end of its tail (Illus. 89). Compared with this "tyrannous king" of the Cretaceous period, the present king of beasts, His Majesty the Lion, is as harmless as a kitten.

In striking contrast to this monster of the past stood another representative of the kangaroo-like reptiles, known as the *ornithomimus.* It was small in stature and distantly resembled the ostriches of today. These peaceful animals probably fed on worms and small insects exclusively and, instead of teeth, had a horny beak resembling that of birds.

Ill. 89. *Tyrannosaurus rex*, a giant kangaroo-like reptile, terror of the Cretaceous period. The same period saw an abundance of horned reptiles; triceratops is the largest known representative of this class.

(Courtesy of the Field Museum of Natural History)

Ill. 90. The diplodocus, its near relative the brontosaurus (weight about 50 tons; 70 feet from nose to tail), or the giant stegosaurus (with heavy armor-plate along the spine) might easily be met in the woods of the Jurassic period.
(Courtesy of the U.S. National Museum)

Besides this large group of dinosaurs, who traveled on hind legs and tail and used their front paws exclusively for feeding purposes or fighting, there was another large branch which closely resembled the lizards of today, except in size. The members of this group probably were the most direct descendants of the early Permian reptiles (Illus. 87), and were less dynamic than their "two-legged" relatives. Traveling through the woods of the Jurassic period, one might easily run into *diplodocus* or his milk brother, the *brontosaurus,* weighing some 50 tons and measuring up to 100 feet from the tip of the nose to the end of the long tail, or into a giant *stegosaurus,* carrying a display of heavy armor-plate along its spine (Illus. 90).

There was no shortage of other kinds of horned reptiles, such as the giant *triceratops* (Illus. 89), for example, or its humbler predecessor, the *protoceratops,* the eggs of which, through a fortunate play of chance, were preserved for the inquiring eyes of surprised present-day paleontologists (Illus. 91).

In making our survey of the powerful Mesozoic kingdom of giant reptiles, we must not forget a large group which, for some reason unsatisfied with terrestrial life, returned to the seas and oceans and adjusted itself to the new conditions in much the same way as the seals, porpoises, and whales of today.* The

* The reader is, of course, aware that the latter animals belong to the class of mammals that returned to the sea at some stage of their evolution.

Ill. 91. Eggs of the dinosaur protoceratops, preserved in the sands of the
Gobi Desert in Mongolia.
(Courtesy of the American Museum of Natural History)

waters of the Mesozoic era were full of different swimming reptiles constantly fighting among themselves for food. The most
typical representatives of the marine reptiles of that time were
the *ichthyosaurus,* rather resembling a fish in its general shape,
and the rather clumsy *plesiosaurus,* which must, however, have
been very successful in its fish-hunting expeditions, because of
its long swan-like neck (Illus. 92).

Among the most bizarre representatives of the great middle
kingdom of reptiles were undoubtedly the *pterodactyls,* which
formed the air force of the empire. These members of the reptile
group, which took to the air, had leatherish wings, naked bodies,
and sharp-toothed mouths (Illus. 93). During the Cretaceous
period, when the kingdom of reptiles was at the peak of its development, these flying monsters reached their maximum size;
specimens have been found measuring up to 25 feet from tip to
tip of their outstretched wings.

Ill. 92. Mesozoic waters abounded with various marine reptiles. Most typical were the ichthyosaurus, generally fishlike in form, and the plesiosaurus, with long, swanlike neck useful for fishing.
(Courtesy of the Field Museum of Natural History)

The flying reptiles of the Mesozoic era represent the transitional stage to the birds of today, as becomes evident from an inspection of some skeletons found in the deposits of the Jurassic period (Illus. 94). The creature that left us these fossilized remains is known as the *archeopteryx* and was a most peculiar combination of a typical flying reptile of the past and the ordinary bird of today. These half-reptiles, half-birds had birdlike plumage, although their sharp teeth, clawed wings, and long conical tails definitely betrayed their reptilian ancestry. One can hardly

Ill. 93. Pterodactyls (upper left), "air force" of the great middle kingdom of reptiles, had naked bodies, leathery wings, and sharp teeth. During the Cretaceous period these flying monsters attained maximum development; some fossil specimens show a 25-foot wingspread. Prehistoric turtle at lower right.
(Courtesy of the Field Museum of Natural History)

Ill. 94. Reading the "Book of Sediments." Some pages of the Jurassic chapter, found in Solenhofen, Bavaria, which revealed the skeleton of the first bird, known as the archeopteryx. The sketch in the lower left corner gives the reconstruction of this creature. *(Courtesy of the U.S. National Museum)*

desire any better specimen to demonstrate the continuity of evolution between such seemingly different groups of animals as reptiles and birds!

The kingdom of giant reptiles, with its innumerable representatives on the land, in the sea, and in the air, was certainly the most powerful and most extensive animal kingdom during the entire existence of life on the Earth, but it also had a most tragic and unexpected end. During a comparatively short period toward the end of the Mesozoic era the tyrannosaurus, stegosaurus, ichthyosaurus, plesiosaurus, and all the other "sauri" disappeared from the surface of the Earth as if wiped away by some giant storm,* leaving the ground free for miniature mammals that had waited for this opportunity for more than 100 million years.

The causes that led to such complete extinction of the most powerful animals that ever existed on the surface of our planet have remained rather obscure. It has often been suggested that the chief cause was the general elevation of the ground in the preparation for the Laramide revolution and the steady approach of more severe climatic conditions. But the extinction of intercontinental seas and marshlands could not have affected a large variety of dinosaurs, which were completely adapted to life on dry land, and we also know that many of the species, such as the pterodactyls, became extinct long before the climate became much cooler. It has also been suggested that the rising kingdom of mammals was directly responsible for the fall of the old reptilian empire. Nobody, of course, thinks that the tiny primitive mammal, not exceeding an ordinary rat in size, could have conquered the dinosaur in an open fight. But it is quite possible that, in their search for food, the mammals were feeding upon dinosaur eggs, thus disastrously reducing the birth rate of these mighty animals. This hypothesis, however, does not explain all the facts, since a number of large reptiles, such as the ichthyosaurus, probably gave birth to living young, and these babies were sufficiently large to defend themselves.

---

* At present the survivors of this mighty kingdom are represented by only a few species, such as crocodiles, alligators, and turtles.

Probably the most general hypothesis that can explain the fall of the reptilian kingdom and many other similar occurrences in other groups of animals is the assumption that the extinction of a race is due to the natural decrease of the birth rate in any old stock of living things. In fact, since each new generation within any given branch of organic evolution is produced by division of the genetic cells of previous generations, one may think that the hereditary properties carried over by the genus become more and more "diluted," and that the cells of the old stock gradually grow *"tired of division."*

Our present knowledge concerning the properties of the living cell and the process of its division is still too meager to tell whether this hypothesis is true or not. But, *a priori*, it does not seem at all impossible that such "exhaustion of living power" can take place, and that entire races of animals and plants can die out simply because they are getting much too old. Such a point of view would also be consistent with the *principle of recapitulation*, according to which the life of each individual repeats in its early embryonic stages all the phases of the development of its race. If the development of an individual parallels the development of the entire race, it would be logical to expect, conversely, that the race itself should die sooner or later in the same way as each of its separate members does.

THE "MILK AGE"

From the point of view of biology, the phrase about acquiring some habits "with one's mother's milk" makes very profound sense, since the presence of mammary glands producing the nourishing whitish liquid is the most fundamental characteristic of a large group of higher animal species to which we ourselves belong. Mammals vary widely in their traits and habits; some even lay eggs, as do the duckbills or the anteaters; but the unbreakable habit of giving good fresh milk to their babies binds them together into one well-defined group. The history of mammals probably dates as far back as the Late Paleozoic era, when the milk-producing organs were first developed in some small-sized reptiles that had become especially thoughtful about bringing up their babies. But through the dark periods of the Mesozoic era, when the land, sea, and air were under the permanent domination of giant reptiles, these humble child-loving animals had very little opportunity to develop. The deposits of the Jurassic period contain occasional remains of these archaic mammals, which were never larger than a very small dog and are most often found in association with the dinosaur, for which they must have been very tasty food. But the fact that these remains are found almost everywhere throughout the world (especially in Africa) indicates that this new type of life was very successful in the struggle for existence and contained in itself infinite possibilities for further development. It is interesting to note that the only place in the world where the fossils of primitive mammals are not found is the continent of Australia, the very same piece of land that is now characterized by the exclusive presence of such primitive mammals as duckbills, spiny anteaters, and kangaroos.* This fact may be considered a sign that the origin of mammals on this isolated continent took place much later and in an entirely independent way from the rest of the world, and it gives some support to the hypothesis that the similarity of many living forms may be connected with general rules of evolution in analogous surroundings rather than being the outcome of direct heredity. As for independent lines of evolution on different continents, one may also speculate regarding the relationship between the relative speed of evolution in different localities and the corresponding areas of available land. Since the progress of living things is achieved by the method of "trial and error," probably mostly error,† one should expect that the rate of such

---

* Kangaroos should be considered a rather primitive form of mammal, since, though they do not lay eggs, they give birth to their babies in not fully developed form and carry them in a skin pouch on the abdomen until they are completely formed.

† Of all the possible changes that can occur spontaneously in a living organism, comparatively few prove to be useful in the struggle for existence and are thus perpetuated by the process of natural selection.

progress will be proportional to the number of individuals involved. Thus evolution should proceed faster on such extensive playgrounds as combined Eurasia and Africa, somewhat slower in the Americas, and much slower on the isolated little continent of Australia.

But we should not go too far into these speculations, which can hardly be conclusively proved or disproved at the present time, and now let us return to the description of the progress of mammals. As we have mentioned, these little animals were merely muddling through during hundreds of millions of years while all the *Lebensraum* on the Earth was entirely conquered by the reptiles. But with the disappearance of the giant reptiles, which took place on the eve of the Laramide revolution, the mammals unexpectedly became the sole potentates of the continents and rapidly developed to the full.

During the Eocene period, which opens the modern age in the history of the animal world, the mammalian kingdom was very extensive and had numerous representatives that can be readily recognized as the ancestors of the animals we know today. But *this primitive world was characterized by the extreme smallness of all the animal forms,* and it took a period of 40 million years for them to grow to their present size. The horses and camels of the Eocene period were about the size of a house cat, slender-bodied rhinoceroses were no larger than a pig, and the ancestors of today's elephants were hardly waist-high to a man. Of course, there was no man, not even a small one, but there were numerous miniature monkeys, which were probably already enjoying themselves by dropping coconuts from the tops of the trees. The beasts of prey were represented by the so-called *creodonts,* which later developed into two large branches of animals, the dog-like (dogs, wolves, bears) and the catlike (cats, tigers, lions).

As time went on some of the early mammalian forms died out, whereas others gradually developed and grew in size. By the time of the Miocene period, some 20 million years ago, horses had grown to the size of Shetland ponies, while the rhinoceros had already become a formidable beast, no longer to be got out of the way by a mere kick. But the mightiest animals of that

Ill. 95. The entelodonts (giant boars), probably the most powerful animals of the Miocene period, were as big as oxen and had skulls 4 feet long. About 20,000,000 years ago the rhinoceros (left background) was a slender beast no bigger than an average dog. The horses of that time (center background) were no larger than today's Shetland ponies, while the prehistoric camels (left background) resembled today's gazelles.

(Courtesy of the Field Museum of Natural History)

time were certainly the giant boars, the *entelodonts*, which were as tall as an ox and had a skull 4 feet long (Illus. 95). The ancestors of today's elephants also grew in size, and their trunks, almost unnoticeable in the early stages of development, grew longer and longer. On the continent of Europe and in Southern Asia, but not in America, one could occasionally meet nasty-looking great apes, known as *Dryopithecus* and distantly related to the gorillas of today.

It must not be forgotten that up to the beginning of the Pleistocene glaciation the climate of the Earth was much milder, with food much more abundant, even in the northern latitudes, and that the animals now found only in the tropics then ranged over large areas of Europe, North America, and Northern Asia. In fact, the fossil remains found in the deposits of that time leave no doubt that elephants, rhinoceroses, hippopotami, lions, ordinary and extinct (saber-toothed) tigers, and many other animals that are now found only in equatorial Africa were hunting for their food over the present sites of the cities of New York, Paris, Moscow, and Peking.

When the large sheets of ice began advancing from the northern regions for the first time, slowly covering large areas of Europe and North America, the animal and plant life of this

Ill. 96. One of the most impressive sights of the glacial periods must have been a family of long-tusked mammoths, covered with thick brown wool, making their way through the deep snow then blanketing large areas of Asia, Europe, and North America.

(Courtesy of the Field Museum of Natural History)

region was slowly pushed southward. Many species, which for one reason or another were unable to migrate farther south, perished from the increasing cold, while the others became accustomed to the new climate and developed long, warm furs protecting them from the frost of the polar winters.

Probably the most impressive sight of these chilly periods of the Earth's history was that of a family of heavily built long-tusked mammoths, covered with thick coats of brownish wool, making their way across the snow-covered continents (Illus. 96). Although this race of giant hairy animals became extinct many thousands of years ago, frozen carcasses of some of them can still be found in the Siberian tundras. One member of an expedition of the Russian Academy of Sciences even ventured to eat a hamburger made of the frozen mammoth meat. Only the presence of a first-aid kit saved him from serious gastric distress.

THE AGE OF MAN

One of the major factors in the development of mammals was that the size of their brains in respect to the size of their bodies was considerably larger than that of their opponents. This could have been the result of their warm-bloodedness, in contradiction to the usual assumption that a cool head is better than a hot one. The development of the brain was especially noticeable in one branch of the mammalian kingdom, which is known as the *Primates*. These were the mammals which took to the trees and, in order to hold on to the branches, developed grasping hands in contrast to the paws and hoofs of the land-walking varieties. Later, when they returned to the ground from the trees, their hind feet lost their branch-grasping ability, while the front feet became even more adapted for handling various objects, be they coconuts, sticks, or stones, or (later) spears, bows, and arrows.

As the reader has undoubtedly already guessed, we are approaching now a discussion of the evolutionary origin of man. The development of man from his less good-looking and less intelligent ancestors has taken place during the last 2 million years. Probably the earliest stage of that branch of organic evolution which led to what we now call Homo sapiens, or thinking man, originated in Africa during the Late Pliocene period. In 1959 the remains of *Zinjanthropus*, who may have been the great-great-great-. . . granddaddy of us all, were found in East Africa by the British archeologist Dr. Louis Leakey. Zinjanthropus — the name means East African man — lived 1,750,000 years ago and is the earliest known maker of stone tools. Fossils of *Australopithecus*, the South African ape-man who lived about two million years ago, were discovered by the British scientist Dr. Raymond Dart in the 1920s, along with bone weapons and the remains of animals Australopithecus had killed.

From the scanty fossil record it appears that these manlike creatures wandered north and eastward, spreading throughout Europe and Asia. In about 500,000 B.C., *Pithecanthropus* lived on the island of Java in the East Indies, and *Sinanthropus* near the present location of Peking in China. Both of these deceased individuals from long ago looked very much alike and are considered by some anthropologists to belong to the same genus. The cavity of the skull which contained the brain was only about 1000 cubic centimeters as compared with the 1500 cubic centimeters of modern man's skull cavity. On the other hand, we must remember that the brain volume of the largest of the modern apes, the gorilla, is only slightly over 500 cubic centimeters. The brows of these individuals, which were advanced enough for us to consider them as our predecessors, receded and the brow ridges above the eyes were very heavy. Pithecanthropus was a family man but not a very sociable one. He lived with his family in the woods and sought shelter in caves. It is likely that he knew how to make fire, and manufactured simple tools and weapons of wood and stone. There are some indications that the same type of pre-man existed in Europe. In fact, a man's jaw found near Heidelberg in Germany may have belonged to that European Pithecanthropus man.

A more advanced stage of the evolution of man, as far as the findings go, is *Homo neanderthalensis*, the remnants of whom are found in considerable number in Asia, Africa, and Europe. His skull was larger than that of the Pithecanthropus man, and so was his skill. He was rather short and stocky, his shoulders were stooped, and his knees were slightly bent like those of modern apes. His face was large, the forehead low, brow arches overhanging, his jaws were animal-like and his chin receding. But in spite of his looks (from our point of view, at least) he was quite a man. He skillfully fashioned beautiful chipped stone tools and weapons and was a great hunter. But he met his competitor in another branch of the human race, known as *Cro-Magnon* man, so-called after a rock shelter called Cro-Magnon in the little village of Les Eyziès in southwestern France where the remnants of his achievement were first discovered. Cro-Magnon man was tall, dark (no doubt), and handsome. His forehead was high, manifesting the growth of the front part of his brain, and his chin was sharp and protruding. He was an expert in weapon-making and hunting, and in his spare time covered the walls of the caves he lived in with beautiful pictures of the animals he hunted. These pictures can easily hold their own by comparison with all the finest paintings produced by modern man. Most probably Cro-Magnon man developed the art of speech, and it is likely that he was also able to express his emotions in music. It is quite possible that there was a bitter competition between the Neanderthal and Cro-Magnon races and that the latter exterminated the former. And so we come to the man of today.

What is the future of humanity as we now know it? From the evolutionary point of view the outlooks are, unfortunately, rather grim. As we have seen, the entire evolution from amoeba to man was the result of the overproduction of progeny, the fight for existence, and the survival of the fittest. This constituted the process of natural selection which led to steady improvement and the progress of living organisms. Today we also have overproduction of human beings, usually referred to as the "population explosion," but it is considered rather as an evil than a valuable evolutionary factor for humanity. The point is, of course, that Homo sapiens in his wisdom developed a code of morals opposing the killing of his own kind, and that the science of medicine does everything possible to prolong the life of sickly individuals who would otherwise die and leave no progeny. Thus the "bad genes" produced by natural mutations are permitted and even encouraged to pass into the following generations instead of being eliminated in the struggle for survival. This fact put the evolution of the human race into reverse and, instead of improving, it is at best kept at the present level with the danger of decline. It is difficult to say how things could be improved in the centuries and millennia to come. Advising families to produce thirteen children, keep the best three, and dispose of the rest is of course out of the question. But the possibility is not excluded that, with the future development of experimental genetics and biochemistry, it will become possible to inspect the gametes (sex cells) before fertilization, and to remove or repair those with badly mutated genes. It may also become possible to operate on the genes in such a way as to improve the future human race, removing the hereditary leftovers such as the appendix, and increasing the size of the brain. If science is able to do this, the human race on the surface of the Earth may flourish for an indefinite time in the future.

POPULATION GROWTH, FOOD, AND POWER

Having many advantages in competition with other creatures

populating the Earth, primitive man began to multipy rapidly and to spread out. By 20,000 B.C. he had crossed the Bering Strait and had colonized the Americas. It may be guessed that some 10,000 years ago Homo sapiens must have numbered about 10 million. For the beginning of the Christian era, a more reliable estimate leads to the figure of 350 million. During the next 2000 years the increase of population was very slight, and it has been estimated that by the beginning of the eighteenth century the population of the Earth had increased to only 500 million. During the last two centuries, however, there has been a rapid growth of the population, which is today 2.8 billion. At the present time the increase of population is proceeding at the rate of about 100,000 more people per day.

The implication of such rapid growth of humanity was first emphasized by Thomas Malthus in *An Essay on Population*, published in 1799. In this book he described the grim prospect for the future of humanity and predicted that in less than a century agriculture and animal husbandry would not be able to feed the increased population of the Earth. His prediction turned out to be wrong, but only because he had not foreseen that during the nineteenth century scientific methods of agriculture would develop to such an extent that the available land could match in food-production the growth of the population.

Today, with all the advances of scientific agriculture, the competition between food increase and population increase is weighted in favor of the latter. Thus, for example, between the years 1947 and 1953 the world's food production increased by 8 per cent, while the world population jumped up by 11 per cent. In his lecture entitled *The Problem of World Population* (Cambridge University Press, 1958) Sir Charles Darwin, who, although a physicist himself, must have inherited the biological interests of his famous grandfather, writes: "The present rapid increase of population cannot possibly be an average condition, but must terminate some day not very far off. If anyone doubts this, mere arithmetic will convince him, for it is easily calculated that if the present rate of increase continued for a thousand years — not a long time in human history — there would still be standing room on the land surface of the Earth, but not room for everybody to lie down. . . ."

But probably long before that the growing population of the Earth will suffer from the shortage of food and power resources. All the food we consume is produced by the photosynthetic action of the Sun's rays in green plants. Humanity either consumes this energy directly, by eating rice, bread, and vegetables, or in an improved though second-hand way by eating cattle and fowl who, in their turn, have consumed the energy first-hand. When the food resources provided by plants that grow on the land are overdrawn, humanity will have to turn its hungry eyes to the vegetation of the oceans, which exceed the land vegetation by a factor of ten. We will have to compete with fish for plankton and also eat the fish themselves as a meat substitute.

In respect to power sources the situation looks equally grim. Today we are using coal and oil, the amount of which is limited. After these resources are exhausted, humanity will be forced to go back to burning wood logs, and the areas of the continents necessary for growing firewood will compete with the areas used to grow foodstuff.

"What about atomic energy?" the reader will ask. Yes, what about it? Today we have uranium-consuming atomic-power plants used either as stationary sources of electric energy or for propulsion purposes. But the light uranium isotope used in these nuclear reactors is very rare in nature, and it is everybody's guess how long it will last. What is worse, with the present uranium reactors large amounts of radioactive fission products are produced which have to be either buried underground or dumped in sealed barrels into the ocean. If we have to build enough uranium reactors to supply all the needs of humanity, assuming that we have enough uranium, the problem of the disposal of fission products may become practically insolvable.

There exists, however, a much more promising and exciting possibility. The energy of the Sun and all the other stars is due to a thermonuclear reaction in which two ordinary hydrogen atoms unite into an atom of heavy hydrogen which subsequently builds up into helium. But few people realize that the energy-

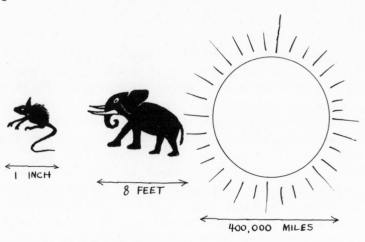

Ill. 97. The rate of heat-production (metabolism) within a body must
decrease with its size.

producing reaction inside the Sun is extremely slow. Indeed, the
amount of heat produced per unit volume in the Sun's interior
is less than one-tenth of 1 per cent of the amount of heat produced in the human body due to metabolic processes. If the
heating unit of an electric coffee pot produced heat at the same
rate as it is produced in the interior of the Sun, it would take
about a year before the water began to boil — provided, of course,
that the coffee pot had perfect thermal insulation and no heat
was lost. Why, then, is the Sun so hot? A simple analogy will
clear up the matter. The total amount of heat produced in the
body of an animal is proportional to its volume, i.e., the space it
occupies measured in cubic units. On the other hand, the heat
is lost through its surface, which is measured in square units of
area. Therefore, the larger the animal, the smaller is its surface
in respect to its volume, and the smaller is the amount of heat
liberation per unit volume needed to maintain its body temperature. For example, an elephant is about 100 times larger than a
mouse and 1 million times heavier. But the area of the elephant's
skin is only 10,000 times that of a mouse. If a mouse were to
metabolize as slowly as an elephant it would freeze to death

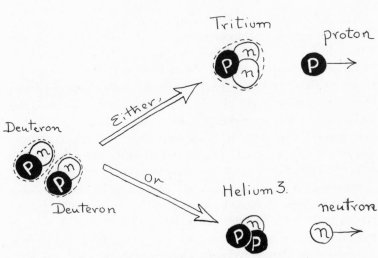

Ill. 98. Two ways in which two deuterons (i.e., nuclei of heavy hydrogen) can react, liberating nuclear energy.

because of large heat losses from the surface. If an elephant were to metabolize as fast as a mouse, it would be a roasted elephant, since the temperature of its body would go way up. Well, the Sun is much larger still than an elephant, and even though the nuclear-energy liberation in its interior is 1000 times slower than the metabolism in man, its surface temperature must be 6000° C. in order to radiate that energy into the surrounding space (Illus. 97).

Thus, even if we could match the thermonuclear process producing energy in the Sun and the stars, it would be of no practical value to us at all. But if, instead of using ordinary hydrogen (as the Sun and other stars do) we use instead "heavy hydrogen," or deuterium, the reactions proceed much faster. It has been calculated that at the temperature of 1 million degrees nuclear reactions in heavy hydrogen will liberate 1 calorie per gram per second (Illus. 98) and at 3 million degrees about 1000 calories per gram per second. (One calorie is defined as the amount of heat necessary to warm up 1 gram of water by 1 degree centigrade.)

It is heavy hydrogen which, being mixed with uranium, produces the many-megaton explosions of so-called H-bombs. But, although it was comparatively easy to construct such bombs, a much more difficult task is the achievement of a controlled thermonuclear reaction in heavy hydrogen, which would liberate energy in a steady flow of any desirable intensity. Work in this direction has been conducted intensively during the last two decades in the United States (Project Sherwood), in the Soviet Union (Project *Brianskie Lesa*), and in other countries, but in spite of all efforts the results so far are negative.

However, as has always been the case in the history of science and technology, if something is possible in principle, human genius will sooner or later put it into practice. And it is likely that the secret of controlled thermonuclear reactions will be broken very soon. Heavy-hydrogen thermonuclear reactors will have terrific advantages over present uranium reactors. Heavy water containing heavy hydrogen forms about 0.02 per cent of ordinary water in the oceans, and its separation from the ordinary water is a well-known and comparatively simple process. Thermonuclear reaction in heavy hydrogen does not produce any dangerous radioactive elements, so that no problem of disposal of reaction products will exist. The main products of the reaction will be fast neutrons and protons that will be used on the spot for turning liberated nuclear energy into electric current or any other form of energy.

It is interesting to calculate how long a time heavy hydrogen contained in the ocean water can serve humanity in the future. The total volume of water in the oceans is 330 million cubic miles, and each cubic mile of water contains 500 million tons of hydrogen. This makes a total of 165,000 trillion tons of hydrogen, 0.02 per cent of which — i.e., 33 trillion tons — is heavy hydrogen. It is known that nuclear reaction in 1 gram of heavy hydrogen liberates 18 billion calories. Thus the total amount of nuclear energy from the heavy hydrogen in sea water is six hundred million sextillion (6 followed by 21 zeros!!) calories.

What is the energy consumption by humanity at the present time? Because of an abundance of energy and a shortage of farmlands in the future, it is reasonable to assume that instead of growing the food, thus utilizing the energy of the Sun's rays, man will synthesize his food from elements, using the nuclear energy of heavy hydrogen. Such synthesis can be achieved with our present knowledge of organic chemistry, and can certainly be made much more economical if mass production becomes necessary. A healthy diet is accepted to be 300 kilogram-calories* (300,000 calories) per person per day, so that to feed the existing 2.8 billion persons on the Earth one needs 300 quadrillion calories per year. About the same amount of energy is used in world production of electric power (mostly by burning coal), and a little more is obtained in burning oil and gasoline. Thus one can say approximately that humanity uses today 1 quintillion calories per year. Assuming 10 per cent for the efficiency of turning nuclear energy into food and mechanical and electric power, and dividing the total amount of stored energy by the annual needs of humanity today, we find that *this stored energy will last for 60 billion years!*

Now remember that our solar system is only 5 billion years old, and according to evidence that will be presented in the next chapter, the Sun is scheduled to shine as it shines today for another 5 billion years. Even if humanity increases tenfold in number, which may approach the limit put by Sir Charles Darwin for availability of standing and reclining room on the surface of our planet, the energy derived from heavy hydrogen in the ocean water will last as long as the Sun lasts. Thus there is no cause to worry for the next 5 billion years of life on Earth. Considering biological arguments given earlier in this chapter, it is not realistic to believe that Homo sapiens, who is less than 100,000 years old, will survive as a species for 5 billion years to come.

It is more likely that the place of Homo sapiens will be taken by some other intelligent species which may develop from some rodent or even from an insect. We do not know.

---

* A kilogram-calorie is equivalent to one unit (known popularly as a calorie) used to express the heating value of food in the diet.

The Future of the Earth

SHORT-RANGE FORECAST

As WE HAVE LEARNED in previous chapters, the history of the Earth during the some 5 billion years of its existence represents a sequence of monotonously repeating changes. The crust buckles because of tectonic activity in the Earth's interior, and high mountain ranges rise over the surface of the continents. The rains slowly wash away these newly formed mountains, depositing the debris at the ocean bottom, and reducing continental surfaces to marshy flatlands. The next crumbling of the crust forms new mountain ranges which, in their turn, are washed away by rains, and so on and so on. Geological evidence indicates that mountain-forming (or orogenic) eras occurred repeatedly in the past with intervals of 100 to 150 million years, and there is no reason to doubt that the future of the Earth's surface will be any different from the past for many more millions of years to come. We are living at the closing stage of the last (Laramide) orogenic era, which started about 70 million years ago. That is why we can enjoy beautiful mountain views, in the Rockies, the Alps, or the Himalayas. As many more millions of years pass by, all the glory of the present mountain landscapes will be washed away, and, for many other millions of years to come, the surfaces of continents will be featureless, marshy, and partially hidden under shallow seas. Then new mountains will rise again, to the great enjoyment of the alpinists, if there are any at that time.

Minor changes of the Earth's surface take place, though slowly, before our eyes. The polar caps, which at present cover about 3 per cent of the Earth's surface and represent the remnants of much more extensive ice sheets that existed during the last glaciation, are slowly melting. As was mentioned in Chapter 6, each year the thickness of these ice sheets is reduced by about two feet, and the water resulting from that melting, being distributed all over the oceans, must raise the ocean level by 1 inch per year, gradually flooding the coastal regions of the continental massives. On the other hand, due to the isostatic equilibrium of the solid crust of the Earth, some areas of the continents are slowly rising up while others are sinking down. The gradual rise of continental surfaces can, at least partially, be attributed to the reduced weight caused by the melting of ice in the polar regions.

Connected with these changes of the surface features are the changes of climatic conditions in various localities. For example, one finds that within the last thirty years the mean annual temperature of North America and northern Europe increased by several degrees. The climatic conditions on the Earth during the past geological eras were quite different from what they are to-day. Only 40,000 years ago thick ice sheets were descending from the northern highlands, extending as far as New York City in North America and beyond the present location of Paris and Berlin in Europe. On the other hand, earlier in the history of the Earth, Greenland, which is now a continuous slab of ice some two miles thick, was covered with woods of such familiar trees as oak and chestnut, and coral reefs were flourishing in the waters where now only icebergs float.

As we have said, the alternating advances and retreats of ice sheets, which profoundly changed the local landscape and climate, were most likely due to small variations of the Earth's orbit in its motion around the Sun. In fact, Milankovich's calculations of the amount of sun-heat received by the Earth during the last 250,000 years stand in very good agreement with the geological data about the variation of climate during that period of time. If Milankovich was right, it should also be possible to predict the climates of the future, since the science of celestial mechanics gives us advance data concerning changes in the Earth's orbital motion for 100,000 years ahead. Such calculations, uncertain as they are, indicate that the present warming-up period in the Northern Hemisphere will continue for some 20,000 years. In the year 5000 the climate of Boston may resemble the present climate of Washington, D.C.; in the year 10,000, that of New Orleans; in the year 15,000, that of Miami; and in the year 20,000, that of the West Indies. Then, because of further changes in the Earth's motion, the situation will reverse and giant tongues of ice will move down again, obliterating such cities as Montreal, Oslo, and Stockholm and threatening Chicago, Boston, and London. This period of extensive glaciation will be followed again by a long warming-up period, and the next glaciation period is not expected until some 900,000 years from now. And so on, and so on, as long as the present-day mountains stand on the surface of the Earth.

When the mountains are washed away by rains and the surface of the continents have become flat again, glaciers will disappear for a long period of time until new mountains are formed again by the next crumbling of the Earth's crust. And so on, and so on, as long as the Sun remains shining in the sky.

LONG-RANGE FORECAST*

But what about the Sun? How long will it shine?

Since practically all that happens on the surface of the Earth depends on light and heat radiation from the Sun, the distant future of the Earth is naturally connected with that of the Sun. We know that the Sun has been supplying the Earth with heat and light for the past 5 billion years. How long will it continue to do so in the future? To answer this question we must know what are the sources of the solar energy which pours out into space at such a tremendous rate.

In olden times the Sun was supposed to be "burning" more or

---

* More detailed discussion of the evolution of stars, and of our sun in particular, will be found in the author's book, *A Star Called the Sun* (a rejuvenation of *The Birth and Death of the Sun*), which is now in preparation.

less in the same way as logs do in the fireplace. In fact, according to the Greek legend, fire was brought to the Earth for the benefit of mankind by a hero called Prometheus. But it is easy to calculate that, even if the body of the Sun were made of a mixture of the best aviation gasoline and pure oxygen, it would not last, at the present rate of burning, for more than just a few thousand years. In the middle of the last century the British physicist Lord Kelvin and the German physicist Hermann von Helmholtz proposed independently of each other a hypothesis which at that time seemed very promising. It is known that gas contained in a cylinder gets heated if it is compressed rapidly by pushing in the piston. Mechanical work done by the hand pushing in the piston is turned into heat, and a definite relation exists between the amount of mechanical work done and the amount of heat produced. Kelvin and Helmholtz visualized the Sun as a giant sphere of gas held together by the forces of Newtonian gravity. When the body of the Sun first condensed from thin interstellar material, it was probably quite cold and non-luminous. However, under the action of mutual gravity forces, this giant sphere of cool gas gradually contracted, and the mechanical work done by these forces turned into heat which warmed the gas. Thus the Sun finally reached its present state with a surface temperature of about 6000° C. and still much higher temperatures in its interior. Accepting that hypothesis, one can calculate that the Sun could have existed for a few hundred million years and still might have about as much time to exist in the future. At the time Kelvin and Helmholtz formulated their hypothesis, that life span for the Sun seemed to be reasonably long, and the contraction theory of solar evolution was accepted without a protest. However, the later expansion of the geological time scale, which required several billion years for the past life of the Sun, brought this theory of solar-energy production into serious difficulties. It seemed that there did not exist in nature an energy source powerful enough to maintain the radiation of the Sun for such a long period of time.

The riddle saw its solution when, late in the last century, the French physicist Henri Becquerel discovered the phenomenon of radioactivity, and early in the present century when the British physicist Lord Rutherford showed that the atoms of light, normally stable elements, can be artificially transformed into one another with the liberation of tremendous amounts of energy. The energy hidden in atomic nuclei exceeds, by the factor of a million, the energy which can be obtained by ordinary chemical reactions such as burning. While the burning of gasoline could maintain the Sun for only a few thousand years, nuclear-energy sources would raise this figure to several billions of years!

A more detailed study of that problem had to wait until more information concerning the physical conditions in the Sun's interior and the rates of nuclear reactions became available. In the early 1920s the British astronomer Sir Arthur Eddington developed a theory of the Sun's interior structure which made it possible to calculate the pressure and temperature that obtained below its luminous surface. He came out with an astonishing result: that the gas in the interior of the Sun is 100 times denser than water (7 times denser than mercury). The temperature of solar material, which is only 6000° C. on the surface, rises to the tremendously high value of 20 million degrees near the center of the Sun.

In the same decade great progress was made in the understanding of nuclear processes. G. Gamow, at that time in Germany, and the team of R. Gurney and E. Condon in the United States, proposed simultaneously the quantum theory of radioactivity, which led to an understanding of why some radioactive elements last for billions of years while others break up in a negligible fraction of a second. Gamow also developed the formula for the rates of artificial transformations of atomic nuclei bombarded by high-energy particles, a formula which stood in perfect agreement with Rutherford's experimental results. Using Eddington's numbers for the physical conditions inside the Sun, and Gamow's formula for the rate of thermonuclear reactions (i.e., nuclear transformations caused by very high temperatures), R. Atkinson from England and F. Houtermans from Austria managed to calculate how much energy could be produced inside the Sun by the thermonuclear reaction between hydrogen and some other light element contained in the Sun's body. Their results stood in very good agreement with the actually observed rates of the Sun's energy production.

Further studies proved that there are two different thermo-nuclear processes involving hydrogen which can be responsible for the energy production in our Sun and in all other stars. The simpler of the two was proposed by the American physicist Charles Critchfield, and begins with a collision between two hydrogen atoms which, because of very high temperature, are reduced to the state of protons. When two protons bump into each other in the hot interior of the star they usually bounce back in the manner of two billiard balls. But occasionally something else happens. While the two protons are in contact at the moment of collision, one of them emits a positive electron and becomes an electrically neutral particle known as a neutron. Since there is no repulsion between protons and neutrons, the two stay together, forming a *deuteron*, the nucleus of the heavy-hydrogen atom, which has the same chemical properties as ordinary hydrogen but is twice as heavy. The next step is a collision between a deuteron formed in this way with another proton. This results in the formation of a helium nucleus which, in contact with ordinary helium, is only three and not four times heavier than hydrogen. Still later, the collision between two helium nuclei of that type results in the formation of ordinary helium and the release of two protons (Illus. 99a). The net result of this sequence of the thermo-nuclear reactions, which is known as the H-H reaction, is the transformation of four hydrogen atoms into one atom of helium, with the liberation of considerable amounts of nuclear energy. At the temperature obtaining in the solar interior, the H-H reaction goes very slowly, requiring 3 billion years for completion. But since 10^{24} (1 followed by twenty-four zeros!) such reactions run simultaneously in every gram of matter within the Sun, the total energy production is just enough to supply it with all the energy necessary to support its radiation.

Another, somewhat more complicated, reaction proposed simultaneously by Hans Bethe in the United States and Carl von Weizsäcker in Germany is known as the *carbon cycle*. In this case the union of four hydrogen atoms into one of helium is accom-

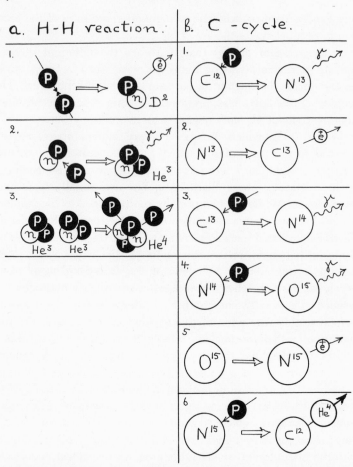

Ill. 99. Two kinds of thermonuclear reactions which take place in the hot interiors of stars. (In *b*, the proton-neutron structure of complex nuclei is not shown.)

plished with the help of a carbon nucleus which captures four protons, one after the other (Illus. 99*b*), and unites them into helium nucleus. In the case of the Sun, the carbon cycle takes only 6 million years, but, because of the low abundance of carbon in solar material, its net energy-production rate is about 100 times lower than that of the direct hydrogen-hydrogen reaction. However, in the case of brighter stars, such as, for example, Sirius, the carbon cycle takes the upper hand over the H-H reaction, and the production of energy follows rather the Bethe-Weizsäcker than the Critchfield scheme. But whatever direction the thermonuclear reaction takes, it always results in the transformation of hydrogen into helium, accompanied by the liberation of very large amounts of nuclear energy.

Since the rate of thermonuclear reactions increases very rapidly with the temperature, most of the energy liberation takes place in the core of the Sun, where the temperature is highest. About 10 per cent of solar matter surrounding its center participates actively in energy production, while the rest forms the outer mantle heated by that energy. Knowing the amount of hydrogen contained in the Sun's reactive core, and the rate at which it is transformed into helium, one calculates that the total life span of the Sun must be about 10 billion years. Since, according to astronomical and geological data, our Sun is about 5 billion years old, we conclude that it still has another 5 billion years to live, during which time it will remain in approximately the same state as today.

What will happen 5 billion years from now, when all the hydrogen contained in the central core of the Sun is exhausted? This question can be answered both from a theoretical and from an observational point of view. Of course, the evolution of stars proceeds so slowly as compared with human history that there is no way to observe it by studying the changes in any one single star. The entire human history and prehistory is just a wink in the life of a star, and no noticeable changes could be expected, even since the time when the first primitive man raised his eyes toward the sky. But there is one important point about stellar evolution. The larger and brighter the star, the faster it goes through its successive evolutionary stages, simply because it uses its hydrogen faster than the fainter stars. Since most of the stars forming our system of the Milky Way must have originated in the same era, about 5 billion years ago, when the Milky Way itself was formed, we should expect that they would today be in different stages of their evolution. Faint stars, using their hydrogen supply very economically, are expected to be now still in their prime, whereas very bright stars, "burning their candles at both ends," must have run out of their hydrogen supply a long time ago or are running out of it right now. Thus, looking at the sky, we see stars in various stages of their evolution — just as kittens, puppies, human babies, and crocodiles born on the same day will be in different stages of growth as the years pass by. This circumstance gives us the possibility of comparing the theoretical predictions concerning the future of our Sun with the observed evolutionary stages of various stars seen in the sky.

What does the theory tell us about the future of the Sun? As mentioned above, the Sun is today in the middle of its expected life span, with 5 billion years behind it and another 5 billion years ahead. When, in that distant future, the hydrogen content in the Sun's core is completely exhausted, very important changes are expected to take place in its structure. With all internal fuel burned, "nuclear fire" will spread out into outer layers which still have untouched amounts of hydrogen. Since that process will bring closer to the surface of the Sun the region where thermonuclear reactions take place, the body of the Sun will begin to expand and the amount of light and heat radiated by it will steadily increase.

At the same time the surface temperature, which is at present about 6000° C., will drop to only half of that value, and the giant disk of the Sun, which will then cover a good part of our sky, will be only red-hot instead of white-hot as it is now. In its expansion, the Sun will swallow the inner planets Mercury and Venus, and its red-hot surface will advance toward the Earth. More detailed calculations than we have now are needed in order to predict whether the Sun will also swallow the Earth and will continue to expand toward Mars, but even if that expansion is checked short of the Earth, our oceans will boil and the surface rocks will become red-hot. The expansion process will proceed comparatively fast from the astronomical point of view, taking only about 100 million years, as compared with the Sun's life span of 10 billion years. If we compare the life span of the Sun with the average life span of a man, this death agony would correspond to the last

six months or a year. But, from the human point of view, the
onset of these conditions will proceed very closely. If the Earth's
temperature is to rise by 200° F. in the course of 100 million years,
the rate of increase will be only 0.0002° F. per century, i.e., considerably smaller than climatic changes caused by local meteorological factors.

Do we have observational evidence supporting this, at first
glance, fantastic prediction? Yes, and plenty of it. As we have
mentioned, stars bigger and brighter than our Sun evolve considerably faster and, while ours is still a middle-aged fellow, these
stars have already reached their doomsday and are in various
stages of dying. Stars known from antiquity under such names as
Antares and Betelgeuse shine in the night sky like bright-red
lanterns and are classified by modern astronomers as *red giants*.
Recent studies have shown that, although these stars are only
several times more massive than our Sun, their diameters exceed
that of the Sun by a factor of several hundred. There is no doubt
that the red giants are stars in which "nuclear fire" is spreading
out from their center, blowing them into giant balls of red-hot
rarefied gas. And there is every certainty that our Sun will come
to that stage 5 billion years from now.

While the present state of the Sun and its future development
into a red giant are well understood on the basis of mathematical
studies of the processes taking place in its interior, we have to
rely mostly on observational evidence concerning the latter stages
of evolution. It seems quite certain that by the time a star reaches
the extreme red-giant stage all the nuclear-energy sources in its
interior are completely exhausted and the only possible future
evolution is a slow contraction accompanied by a steady decrease
of brightness. Stars observed in that stage of evolution show very
peculiar and unsteady behavior. Whereas normal (adult) stars
like our Sun today and red-giant (elderly) stars like Betelgeuse
shine with even brightness, the contractive stage of stellar evolution is characterized by a great variability in brightness. At first
the body of a contracting star goes through a series of pulsations,
with its brightness increasing and diminishing in periods varying
from one day to a year (the Cepheid stage). Later on, these regu-

lar pulsations change to periodic mild explosions (U-Geminorum stage) which gradually become less and less frequent but more and more violent. The end of the road, which is reached in a few hundred million years, is marked by a violent explosion known as the *supernova* phenomenon. Just overnight the star becomes billions of times brighter than it was the day before, and a large part of its material is thrown into the surrounding space at tremendous velocities of thousands of miles per second. In the course of a year or two the magnificent fireworks fade out, and what is left of the star is observed as a very small but intensively hot body which emits light only because of very large amounts of heat stored in its interior. Those so-called *white dwarf* stars, a dozen or two of which are found in our region of the Milky Way, are dead stars which have not yet cooled off and become dark, cold remnants of a full and rich stellar life.

What will happen to our Earth when the Sun, some 5 billion years from now, goes through these last agonies of stellar death? The heat developed by the explosion will no doubt melt all the planets which had been living peacefully with the Sun for 10 billion years, and streams of hot gases emanating from the exploding Sun may even throw the molten planets clear out of the solar system. When the force of the explosion is spent, what is left of the Sun and its planets will gradually cool to the temperature of the interstellar space, which is hundreds of degrees below freezing.

The poet Robert Frost wrote:

> *Some say the world will end in fire,*
> *Some say in ice. . . .*

Both these forecasts are certainly correct!

INDEX